ARGOPREP

7th GRADE COMMON CORE
ELA

ENGLISH LANGUAGE ARTS

DAILY PRACTICE BOOK

ARGOPREP.COM

FREE ONLINE SYSTEM WITH VIDEO EXPLANATIONS

ArgoPrep is one of the leading providers of supplemental educational products and services. We offer affordable and effective test prep solutions to educators, parents and students. Learning should be fun and easy! For that reason, most of our workbooks come with detailed video answer explanations taught by one of our fabulous instructors.

Our goal is to make your life easier, so let us know how we can help you by e-mailing us at: info@argoprep.com.

ArgoPrep has won **over 10+ educational awards** for their workbooks and online learning platform. Here are a few highlighted awards!

AWARDS

COOL TOOL

AWARDS

LEADERSHIP

ARGOPREP

OTHER BOOKS BY ARGOPREP

Here are some other test prep workbooks by ArgoPrep you may be interested in. All of our workbooks come equipped with detailed video explanations to make your learning experience a breeze! Visit us at *www.argoprep.com*

COMMON CORE MATH SERIES

COMMON CORE ELA SERIES

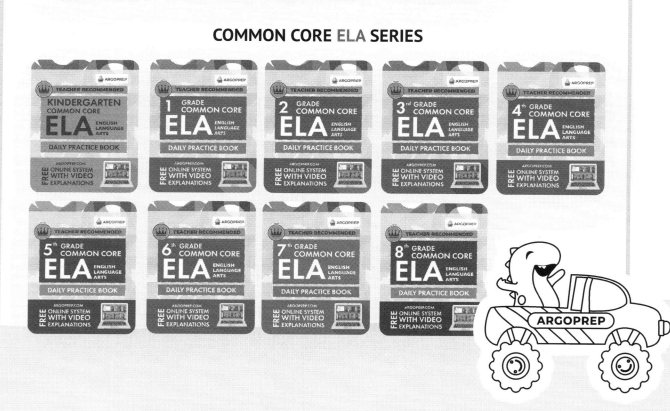

INTRODUCING MATH!

Introducing Math! by ArgoPrep is an award-winning series created by certified teachers to provide students with high-quality practice problems. Our workbooks include topic overviews with instruction, practice questions, answer explanations along with digital access to video explanations. Practice in confidence - with ArgoPrep!

 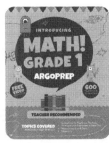 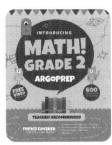 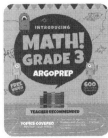 

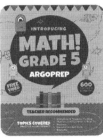  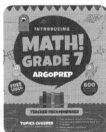 

SCIENCE SERIES

Science Daily Practice Workbook by ArgoPrep is an award-winning series created by certified science teachers to help build mastery of foundational science skills. Our workbooks explore science topics in depth with ArgoPrep's 5 E'S to build science mastery.

KIDS SUMMER ACADEMY SERIES

ArgoPrep's Kids Summer Academy series helps prevent summer learning loss and gets students ready for their new school year by reinforcing core foundations in math, english and science. Our workbooks also introduce new concepts so students can get a head start and be on top of their game for the new school year!

TABLE OF CONTENTS

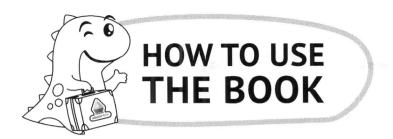

HOW TO USE THE BOOK

This workbook is designed to give lots of practice with the English Common Core State Standards (CCSS). By practicing and mastering this entire workbook, your child will become very familiar and comfortable with the ELA state exam. If you are a teacher using this workbook for your student's, you will notice each question is labeled with the specific standard so you can easily assign your students problems in the workbook. This workbook takes the CCSS and divides them up among 20 weeks. By working on these problems on a daily basis, students will be able to (1) find any deficiencies in their understanding and/or practice of English and (2) have small successes each day that will build proficiency and confidence in their abilities.

You can find detailed video explanations to each problem in the book by visiting:
www.argoprep.com/ela7

We strongly recommend watching the videos, as they will reinforce the fundamental concepts.

IMPORTANT

If you are a teacher or school using this workbook for students, you must purchase a school license to get permission for classroom use. Please email us at info@argoprep.com to obtain a school license.

Go to **argoprep.com/ela7**
OR scan the QR Code:

WEEK 1

Adapted from The Adventure of the Speckled Band *by Sir Arthur Conan Doyle*

Read the passage below. Then answer the questions that follow.

1. On glancing over my notes of the seventy odd cases in which I have during the last eight years studied the methods of my friend Sherlock Holmes, I find many tragic, some comic, a large number merely strange, but none commonplace. He refused to associate himself with any investigation which did not tend towards the unusual, and even the fantastic. I remember one case quite well.

2. It was early in April in the year 1883 that I woke one morning to find Sherlock Holmes standing, fully dressed, by the side of my bed. He was a late riser, as a rule, and as the clock on the mantelpiece showed me that it was only a quarter-past seven, I blinked up at him in some surprise, and perhaps just a little resentment, for I was myself regular in my habits.

3. "Very sorry to wake you up, Watson," said he, "but it's the common lot this morning.

4. "What is it, then — a fire?"

5. "No; a client. It seems that a young lady has arrived in a considerable state of excitement, who insists upon seeing me. She is waiting now in the sitting-room. Now, when young ladies wander about the metropolis at this hour of the morning, and knock sleepy people up out of their beds, I presume that it is something very pressing which they have to communicate. Should it prove to be an interesting case, you would, I am sure, wish to follow it from the outset. I thought, at any rate, that I should call you and give you the chance."

6. "My dear fellow, I would not miss it for anything."

7. I had no keener pleasure than in following Holmes in his professional investigations, and in admiring the rapid deductions, as swift as intuitions, and yet always founded on a logical basis with which he unravelled the problems which were submitted to him. I rapidly threw on my clothes and was ready in a few minutes to accompany my friend down to the sitting-room. A lady dressed in black and heavily veiled, who had been sitting in the window, rose as we entered.

8. "Good-morning, madam," said Holmes cheerily. "My name is Sherlock Holmes. This is my close friend and associate, Dr. Watson, before whom you can speak as freely as before myself. Ha! I am glad to see that Mrs. Hudson has had the good sense to light the fire. Sit near it, and I shall order you a cup of hot coffee, for I observe that you are shivering."

9. "It is not cold which makes me shiver," said the woman in a low voice, changing her seat as requested.

10. "What, then?"

11. "It is fear, Mr. Holmes. It is terror." She raised her veil as she spoke, and we could see that she was indeed in a pitiable state of agitation, her face all drawn and grey, with restless frightened eyes, like those of some hunted animal. Her features and figure were those of a woman of thirty, but her hair was shot with premature grey, and her expression was weary and haggard. Sherlock Holmes ran her over with one of his quick, all-comprehensive glances.

12. "You must not fear," he said soothingly, bending forward and patting her forearm. "We shall soon set matters right, I have no doubt. You have come in by train this morning, I see."

13. "You know me, then?"

14. "No, but I observe the second half of a return ticket in the palm of your left glove. You must have started early, and yet you had a good drive in a dog-cart, along heavy roads, before you reached the station."

15. The lady gave a violent start and stared in bewilderment at my companion.

16. "There is no mystery, my dear madam," he said, smiling. "The left arm of your jacket is spattered with mud in no less than seven places. The marks are perfectly fresh. There is no vehicle save a dog-cart which throws up mud in that way, and then only when you sit on the left-hand side of the driver."

17. "Whatever your reasons may be, you are perfectly correct," she said. "I started from home before six, reached Leatherhead at twenty past, and came in by the first train to Waterloo. Sir, I can stand this strain no longer; I shall go mad if it continues. I have no one to turn to — none, save only one, who cares for me, and he, poor fellow, can be of little aid. I have heard of you, Mr. Holmes; I have heard of you from Mrs. Farintosh, whom you helped in the hour of her sore need. It was from her that I had your address.

18. Oh, sir, do you not think that you could help me, too, and at least throw a little light through the dense darkness which surrounds me? At present it is out of my power to reward you for your services, but in a month or six weeks I shall be married, with the control of my own income, and then at least you shall not find me ungrateful."

19. Holmes turned to his desk and, unlocking it, drew out a small case-book, which he consulted.

20. "Farintosh," said he. "Ah yes, I recall the case; it was concerned with an opal tiara. I think it was before your time, Watson. I can only say, madam, that I shall be happy to devote the same care to your case as I did to that of your friend. As to reward, my profession is its own reward; but you are at liberty to defray whatever expenses I may be put to, at the time which suits you best. And now I beg that you will lay before us everything that may help us in forming an opinion upon the matter."

TIP
of the DAY

Pay attention to how how the author describes each character's dialogue. Those descriptions can help you better understand the story.

EXERCISES

1. Which words in paragraph 1 contrast with the meaning of the word "commonplace"?

   A. notes, cases
   B. methods, number
   C. strange, unusual
   D. investigation, fantastic

   CCSS.ELA-LITERACY.RL.7.4

4. Which detail from the text states that Holmes uses intelligence to solve his cases?

   A. "considerable state of excitement'"
   B. "'I would not miss it for anything'"
   C. "no keener pleasure"
   D. "always founded on a logical basis"

   CCSS.ELA-LITERACY.RL.7.1

2. How does paragraph 2 impact the story?

   A. Holmes and Watson are in conflict, which creates a dark mood.
   B. Holmes surprises Watson by waking him up early, which foreshadows the mysteries that follow.
   C. The interaction between Holmes and Watson supports the theme of the story.
   D. Holmes and Watson find a solution to a problem.

   CCSS.ELA-LITERACY.RL.7.3

5. Why does the narrator describe the lady's appearance in paragraph 11? Select the best answer.

   A. Her appearance exhibits that she is a weak woman.
   B. Her appearance emphasizes that she is dealing with a frightening issue.
   C. Her appearance suggests that she is a wealthy woman.
   D. Her appearance proves that she is an elderly woman.

   CCSS.ELA-LITERACY.RL.7.6

3. What does the word "pressing" mean in paragraph 5?

   A. important
   B. strong
   C. dangerous
   D. helpful

   CCSS.ELA-LITERACY.RL.7.4

6. Which detail from the story indicates how Holmes surprises the lady?

   A. "...I observe that you are shivering."
   B. "You have come in by train this morning, I see."
   C. "...you had a good drive in a dog-cart, along heavy roads, before you reached the station."
   D. "I can only say, madam, that I shall be happy to devote the same care to your case as I did to that of your friend."

   CCSS.ELA-LITERACY.RL.7.2

14

Adapted from Narrative Of The Life of Frederick Douglass *by Frederick Douglass*

Frederick Douglass was born into slavery around 1818 in Maryland. He later wrote several autobiographies about his experiences as a slave and became an important leader in the movement to abolish slavery. In this excerpt from his autobiography, Douglass describes his childhood as a slave.

1. I lived in Master Hugh's family about seven years. During this time, I succeeded in learning to read and write. To accomplish this, I used various strategies. I had no regular teacher. Mrs. Hugh had kindly begun to teach me, but with the advice and direction of her husband, she ceased to instruct me. She also commanded that I not be taught by anyone else.

2. Nothing seemed to make her more angry than to see me with a newspaper. She seemed to think that here lay the danger. I have had her rush at me with a face made all up of fury, and snatch from me a newspaper, in a manner that fully revealed her apprehension. She was an apt woman; and a little experience soon demonstrated, to her satisfaction, that education and slavery were incompatible with each other.

3. From this time I was most narrowly watched. If I was in a separate room any considerable length of time, I was sure to be suspected of having a book, and was at once called to give an account of myself. All this, however, was too late. The first step had been taken. In teaching me the alphabet, she had given me the inch, and no precaution could prevent me from taking the yard.

4. The plan which I adopted, and the one by which I was most successful, was that of making friends of all the little white boys whom I met in the street. As many of these as I could, I converted into teachers. With their kindly aid, obtained at different times and in different places, I finally succeeded in learning to read. When I was sent to do errands, I always took my book with me, and by completing one part of my errand quickly, I found time to get a lesson before my return. I used also to carry bread with me, enough of which was always in the house, and to which I was always welcome; for I was much better off in this regard than many of the poor white children in our neighborhood. This bread I used to bestow upon the hungry little urchins, who, in return, would give me that more valuable bread of knowledge.

5. I used to talk this matter of slavery over with them. I would sometimes say to them that I wished I could be as free as they would be when they got to be men. "You will be free as soon as you are twenty-one, but I am a slave for life! Have not I as good a right to be free as you have?" These words used to trouble them; they would express the greatest sympathy, and console me with the hope that something would occur by which I might be free.

TIP of the DAY

An autobiography is an author's life story.

EXERCISES

1. What is a synonym for the word "ceased" found in paragraph 1?

   A. helped
   B. stopped
   C. struggled
   D. forgot

   CCSS.ELA-LITERACY.RI.7.4

2. What role does paragraph 2 play in the development of the passage?

   A. It details the setting and its relationship to the central idea.
   B. It presents a comparison of two similar ideas.
   C. It explains a major obstacle that Douglass faces.
   D. It describes the steps in solving a problem.

   CCSS.ELA-LITERACY.RI.7.5

3. How does the following statement from paragraph 3 help develop a central idea of the passage?

   In teaching me the alphabet, she had given me the *inch*, and no precaution could prevent me from taking the *yard*.

   A. Douglass plans to learn mathematics, in addition to reading.
   B. Douglass has grown angry about his situation as a slave.
   C. Douglass is grateful for Mrs. Hughes, despite what Master Hughes has demanded.
   D. Douglass will learn how to read, despite the challenges in his household.

   CCSS.ELA-LITERACY.RI.7.2

4. Which paragraph in the passage exhibits the most contrast from paragraph 5?

   A. paragraph 1
   B. paragraph 2
   C. paragraph 3
   D. paragraph 4

   CCSS.ELA-LITERACY.RI.7.5

5. What impact does the phrase "bread of knowledge" have in paragraph 4?

   A. It helps develop the serious tone in the paragraph.
   B. It supports how important bread is as a main topic.
   C. It emphasizes how much Douglass values education.
   D. It explains how Douglass rewards the boys.

   CCSS.ELA-LITERACY.RI.7.1

6. According to Douglass, what is one way he is more fortunate than the boys who help him?

   A. He has access to bread, while the boys do not have enough food.
   B. He is wealthy, while the boys are poor.
   C. He is learning how to read, while the boys are uneducated.
   D. He is allowed to help with errands, while the boys must follow strict rules.

   CCSS.ELA-LITERACY.RI.7.3

A Day *by Emily Dickinson*

I'll tell you how the sun rose, —
A ribbon at a time.
The steeples swam in amethyst,
The news like squirrels ran.

The hills untied their bonnets,
The bobolinks begun.
Then I said softly to myself,
"That must have been the sun!"

But how he set, I know not.
There seemed a purple stile
Which little yellow boys and girls
Were climbing all the while

Till when they reached the other side,
A dominie in gray
Put gently up the evening bars,
And led the flock away.

TIP *of the* DAY

Poems often have a rhythm, or a flow and beat, similar to music.

17

EXERCISES

1. What is the meaning of the first stanza? Use two details from the poem in your response.

_____

_____

_____

_____

CCSS.ELA-LITERACY.RL.7.2

4. What does "Which little yellow boys and girls / Were climbing all the while" mean?

   A. The line describes yellow flowers.
   B. The line explains the behavior of animals.
   C. The line represents clouds and their color at that time of day.
   D. The line emphasizes that children love to play.

CCSS.ELA-LITERACY.RL.7.4

2. When does the poem's rhythm begin to change? Use two details from the poem to describe the change.

_____

_____

_____

_____

CCSS.ELA-LITERACY.RL.7.4

5. Which two stanzas contain similar imagery? Select the answer that contains the correct stanzas and imagery.

   A. Stanzas 1 and 3 describe children sleeping.
   B. Stanzas 1 and 3 describe the sky as purple.
   C. Stanzas 1 and 4 describe the sun rising.
   D. Stanzas 2 and 4 describe leaving home.

CCSS.ELA-LITERACY.RL.7.5

3. What is the impact of the line "the hills untied their bonnets" in stanza 2?

   A. It emphasizes how warm the sun is.
   B. It creates a negative mood in the stanza.
   C. It changes the rhyming scheme in the poem.
   D. It adds to the imagery of the sun beginning to cover the land.

CCSS.ELA-LITERACY.RL.7.4

6. What is the meaning of the final stanza?

   A. Children are going home for the evening.
   B. The weather is rainy.
   C. The sun has set.
   D. A farmer is leading sheep over a hill.

CCSS.ELA-LITERACY.RL.7.5

WEEK 2

: VIDEO ▶
• EXPLANATIONS

ARGOPREP.COM

Phrases

CCSS.ELA-LITERACY.L.7.1.A

Key Terms

What is a phrase?

A phrase is a group of related words in a sentence. A phrase does not have both a subject and a predicate.

Types of phrases can include prepositional phrases, appositives phrases, infinitive phrases, and gerund phrases.

A <u>prepositional phrase</u> starts with a preposition. It can modify a noun (adjective phrase), or it can modify a verb or adverb (adverb phrase).

An <u>appositive phrase</u> emphasizes or renames a word or phrase.

An <u>infinitive phrase</u> starts with the word "to" and a verb.

A <u>gerund phrase</u> is a verbal that ends in "ing." The phrase acts as a noun.

Examples

The following are examples of phrases.

Prepositional phrases:

Becca left her backpack <u>in the house</u>.

<u>After school</u> we played video games.

Appositive phrases:

Grumpy Cat, <u>a famous cat</u>, always frowns.

Frozen, <u>Carly's favorite movie</u>, is animated.

Infinitive phrases:

<u>To love a dog</u> is the best feeling.

Ellen's plan <u>to study all night</u> did not work.

Gerund phrases:

<u>Eating pizza</u> makes Julio happy.

Carlton's favorite activity is <u>swimming in the ocean</u>.

TIP of the DAY

Prepositions describe time (when) or location (where).

What type of phrase is the underlined phrase? Select the correct answer.

Identify the phrase in each sentence. Write the phrase in each space below.

1. <u>Playing the cello</u> takes dedication and practice.

   A. prepositional phrase
   B. appositive phrase
   C. infinitive phrase
   D. gerund phrase

   CCSS.ELA-LITERACY.L.7.1.A

4. We love singing pop songs.

   _____

   _____

   CCSS.ELA-LITERACY.L.7.1.A

2. My dad loves <u>to cook spaghetti.</u>

   A. prepositional phrase
   B. appositive phrase
   C. infinitive phrase
   D. gerund phrase

   CCSS.ELA-LITERACY.L.7.1.A

5. During the movie, we ate popcorn.

   _____

   _____

   _____

   CCSS.ELA-LITERACY.L.7.1.A

3. Tasha hiked <u>into the forest.</u>

   A. prepositional phrase
   B. appositive phrase
   C. infinitive phrase
   D. gerund phrase

   CCSS.ELA-LITERACY.L.7.1.A

6. Craig's best friends, Hannah and Danny, are thirteen years old.

   _____

   _____

   CCSS.ELA-LITERACY.L.7.1.A

Clauses

CCSS.ELA-LITERACY.L.7.1.A

Key Terms

What is a clause?

A clause is a group of words that contains both a subject and a predicate.
A clause can stand alone as a complete sentence, or a clause can be part of a sentence.
There are two types of clauses. As a review, clauses contain both a subject and a predicate.

What is an independent clause?

An independent clause can stand on its own as a sentence. It expresses a complete thought.
A simple sentence is an example of an independent clause.
Some sentences have an independent clause and a dependent clause. The clause that can stand on its own is the independent clause.

What is a dependent clause?

A dependent clause is a clause that is part of a sentence. A dependent clause cannot stand on its own. It does not express a complete thought.
A dependent clause needs to be added on to an independent clause in order to complete a sentence.
Dependent clauses begin with subordinating conjunctions.

The following is a list of subordinating conjunctions:

After	How	Unless	Which
Although	If	Until	While
As	Since	When	Who
As if	So that	Whenever	Whom
As though	Than	Where	Whose
Because	That	Wherever	
Before	Though	Whether	

Examples

Independent clauses:

Unless you leave now, <u>you will be late for dance class.</u>
<u>I prefer puppies</u>, although kittens are cute.

Dependent clauses:

<u>Since Jeremy is now sixteen</u>, he can drive a car.
I won an award <u>because I worked hard.</u>

TIP
of the
DAY

Reading a clause out loud can help you figure out if it can stand on its own or not.

EXERCISES

What type of clause is the underlined clause? Write dependent or independent in each space below.

1. <u>Alexis laughed at her sister</u> when she burped.

CCSS.ELA-LITERACY.L.7.1.A

2. Miguel passed the ball <u>since Derek was closer to the goal</u>.

CCSS.ELA-LITERACY.L.7.1.A

Identify the dependent clause in each sentence. Write the clause in each space below.

3. The toddler had a timeout because he threw his food.

CCSS.ELA-LITERACY.L.7.1.A

4. While we waited, we looked at our phones.

CCSS.ELA-LITERACY.L.7.1.A

Identify the independent clause in each sentence. Write the clause in each space below.

5. Bryce would rather eat lima beans than clean his room.

CCSS.ELA-LITERACY.L.7.1.A

6. Since the store closed, we could not buy the new video game.

CCSS.ELA-LITERACY.L.7.1.A

WEEK 2 : FRIDAY

Misplaced and Dangling Modifiers

CCSS.ELA-LITERACY.L.7.1.C

Key Terms

What are modifiers?

A modifier is a word, phrase, or clause that describes. It describes another word, phrase, or clause in the sentence. Modifiers act as adjectives or adverbs.

What are misplaced modifiers?

A modifier needs to be placed next to what it is describing. A misplaced modifier is too far away from what it is describing. This makes the sentence confusing. Sentences with misplaced modifiers need to be rewritten.

What are dangling modifiers?

A dangling modifier describes something that has been left out of the sentence. This makes the description unclear. Sentences with dangling modifiers also need to be rewritten.

Examples

Sentence with misplaced modifier:
   My dad sent back his food to the chef <u>that was cold.</u>

Corrected sentence:
   My dad sent back his food that was cold to the chef.

Sentence with misplaced modifier:
   Carla baked cookies for the children <u>with chocolate chips.</u>

Corrected sentence:
   Carla baked cookies with chocolate chips for the children.

Sentence with dangling modifier:
   Playing soccer in the rain, the grass was very slick.

Corrected sentence:
   While the team was playing soccer in the rain, the grass was very slick.

Sentence with dangling modifier:
   Driving to the store, the baby cried.

Corrected sentence:
   As Kate was driving to the store, the baby cried.

Modifiers can act as adjectives or adverbs. Adjectives describe nouns or pronouns. Adverbs describe verbs, adjectives, or other adverbs.

EXERCISES

Read each sentence. Then select the correct answer below.

Each sentence below contains either a misplaced modifier or a dangling modifier. Correctly rewrite each sentence.

1. Tonya was petting the cat eating a candy bar.

   A. contains a misplaced modifier
   B. contains a dangling modifier
   C. is correct as written
   D. contains no modifier

   CCSS.ELA-LITERACY.L.7.1.C

4. While standing in line for movie tickets, lightning flashed.

   CCSS.ELA-LITERACY.L.7.1.C

2. After the football game, the leftover pizza went into the refrigerator.

   A. contains a misplaced modifier
   B. contains a dangling modifier
   C. is correct as written
   D. contains no modifier

   CCSS.ELA-LITERACY.L.7.1.C

5. The girl danced on the stage with curly brown hair.

   CCSS.ELA-LITERACY.L.7.1.C

3. While singing a high note, the crowd clapped for the singer.

   A. contains a misplaced modifier
   B. contains a dangling modifier
   C. is correct as written
   D. contains no modifier

   CCSS.ELA-LITERACY.L.7.1.C

6. The man walked the dog in a pinstriped suit.

   CCSS.ELA-LITERACY.L.7.1.C

WEEK 3

:VIDEO
EXPLANATIONS ▶

ARGOPREP.COM

Adapted from The Adventures of Tom Sawyer
by Mark Twain

The Adventures of Tom Sawyer is a novel that follows the adventures of a young boy in 1840s Mississippi. Read the story and then answer the questions that follow.

1. There comes a time in every rightly – constructed boy's life when he has a raging desire to go somewhere and dig for hidden treasure. This desire suddenly came upon Tom one day. He sallied out to find Joe Harper, but failed of success. Next he sought Ben Rogers; he had gone fishing. Presently he stumbled upon Huck Finn the Red – Handed. Huck would answer. Tom took him to a private place and opened the matter to him confidentially. Huck was willing. Huck was always willing to take a hand in any enterprise that offered entertainment and required no capital, for he had a troublesome superabundance of that sort of time which is not money. "Where'll we dig?" said Huck.

2. "Oh, most anywhere."

3. "Why, is it hid all around?"

4. "No, indeed it ain't. It's hid in mighty particular places, Huck — sometimes on islands, sometimes in rotten chests under the end of a limb of an old dead tree, just where the shadow falls at midnight; but mostly under the floor in haunted houses."

5. "Who hides it?"

6. "Why, robbers, of course — who'd you reckon? Sunday — school superintendents?" said Tom.

7. "I don't know. If 'twas mine I wouldn't hide it; I'd spend it and have a good time."

8. "So would I. But robbers don't do that way. They always hide it and leave it there."

9. "Don't they come after it any more?" asked Huck.

10. "No, they think they will, but they generally forget the marks, or else they die. Anyway, it lays there a long time and gets rusty; and by and by somebody finds an old yellow paper that tells how to find the marks — a paper that's got to be ciphered over about a week because it's mostly signs and hieroglyphics."

11. "Hyro--which?" Huck asked.

12. "Hieroglyphics — pictures and things, you know, that don't seem to mean anything."

13. "Have you got one of them papers, Tom?"

14. "No."

15. "Well then, how you going to find the marks?"

16. "I don't want any marks. They always bury it under a haunted house or on an island, or under a dead tree that's got one limb sticking out. Well, we've tried Jackson's Island a little, and we can try it again some time; and there's the old hu'nted house up the Still–House branch, and there's lots of dead – limb trees — dead loads of 'em," explained Tom.

17. "Is it under all of them?"

18. "No!" exclaimed Tom.

19. "Then how you going to know which one to go for?"

20. "Go for all of 'em!" Tom replied.

21. "Why, Tom, it'll take all summer."

22. "Well, what of that? Suppose you find a brass pot with a hundred dollars in it, all rusty and gray, or rotten chest full of diamonds. How's that?"

23. Huck's eyes glowed.

24. "That's bully. Plenty bully enough for me. Just you gimme the hundred dollars and I don't want no diamonds."

25. "All right. But I bet you I ain't going to throw off on diamonds. Some of 'em's worth twenty dollars apiece — there ain't any, hardly, but it's worth six bits or a dollar," explained Tom.

26. "No! Is that so?"

27. "Cert'nly — anybody'll tell you so. Hain't you ever seen one, Huck?"

28. "Not as I remember."

29. "Oh, kings have slathers of them."

30. "Well, I don't know no kings, Tom."

31. "I reckon you don't. But if you was to go to Europe, you'd see a raft of 'em hopping around."

32. "Do they hop?" asked Huck.

33. "Hop? No!"

34. "Well, what did you say they did, for?" Huck wondered.

35. "Shucks, I only meant you'd SEE 'em — not hopping, of course — what do they want to hop for? — but I mean you'd just see 'em — scattered around, you know, in a kind of a general way. Like that old humpbacked King Richard."

36. "Richard? What's his other name?"

37. "He didn't have any other name. Kings don't have any but a given name," said Tom.

38. "No?"

39. "They don't," insisted Tom.

40. "Well, if they like it, Tom, all right; but I don't want to be a king and have only just a given name. But say — where you going to dig first?" Huck asked.

41. "Well, I don't know. S'pose we tackle that old dead-limb tree on the hill the other side of Still-House branch?"

42. "I'm agreed," said Huck.

43. So they got a crippled pick and a shovel, and set out on their three-mile tramp. They arrived hot and panting, and threw themselves down in the shade of a neighboring elm to rest.

44. "I like this," said Tom.

45. "So do I."

46. "Say, Huck, if we find a treasure here, what you going to do with your share?" asked Tom.

47. "Well, I'll have pie and a glass of soda every day, and I'll go to every circus that comes along. I bet I'll have a good time," Huck said.

48. "Well, ain't you going to save any of it?"

49. "Save it? What for?"

50. "Why, so as to have something to live on, by and by."

51. "Oh, that ain't any use. Pap would come back to thish-yer town some day and get his claws on it if I didn't hurry up, and I tell you he'd clean it out pretty quick. What you going to do with yours, Tom?"

52. "I'm going to buy a new drum, and a sure-'nough sword, and a red necktie and a bull pup, and get married."

53. "Married!" exclaimed Huck.

54. "That's it."

55. "Tom, you — why, you ain't in your right mind."

56. "Wait — you'll see."

57. "Well, that's the foolishest thing you could do. Look at pap and my mother. Fight! Why, they used to fight all the time. I remember, mighty well," said Huck.

58. "That ain't anything. The girl I'm going to marry won't fight," Tom said.

59. "Tom, I reckon they're all alike. Now you better think 'bout this awhile. I tell you you better. What's the name of the gal?"

60. "It ain't a gal at all — it's a girl," Tom replied.

61. "It's all the same, I reckon; some says gal, some says girl — both's right, like enough. Anyway, what's her name, Tom?"

62. "I'll tell you some time — not now."

63. "All right — that'll do. Only if you get married, I'll be more lonesomer than ever," said Huck

64. "No you won't. You'll come and live with me. Now stir out of this and we'll go to digging."

EXERCISES

1. Based only on the details in paragraph 1, which statement best characterizes Huck?

   A. He wants to find someone to treasure hunt with him.
   B. He is loyal to his friends no matter what happens.
   C. He likes to have fun, but he does not have money.
   D. He is unsure about treasure hunting.

   CCSS.ELA-LITERACY.RL.7.1

2. Which detail from the story best supports your answer in question 1?

   A. "...a raging desire to go somewhere and dig for hidden treasure."
   B. "...took him to a private place and opened the matter to him confidentially."
   C. "...always willing to take a hand in any enterprise that offered entertainment and required no capital..."
   D. "'Where'll we dig?' said Huck."

   CCSS.ELA-LITERACY.RL.7.1

3. Based on your answer in question 2, what impact does this type of language have on the story? Select the best answer.

   A. It emphasizes how creative Tom is when solving problems.
   B. It describes the setting so that the reader can picture the environment around Tom and Huck.
   C. It strengthens the theme of the story.
   D. It draws the reader into the story as if the reader were a first-hand witness.

   CCSS.ELA-LITERACY.RL.7.4

4. What type of language does the author include throughout the characters' dialogue in the story?

   A. metaphors and similes
   B. contractions and slang
   C. personification
   D. alliteration

   CCSS.ELA-LITERACY.RL.7.4

5. Which statement best describes Huck and Tom's conversations?

   A. Huck often does not understand, and Tom becomes annoyed.
   B. Huck helps educate Tom, and Tom is grateful.
   C. Huck and Tom argue about how to solve problems.
   D. Huck tells many stories, and Tom is a thoughtful listener.

   CCSS.ELA-LITERACY.RL.7.6

6. Why does Huck say, "I'll be more lonesomer than ever" to Tom?

   A. Once they find the treasure, they will not spend as much time together.
   B. Huck feels that Tom will not spend as much time with him if Tom gets married.
   C. Huck will be punished if his parents find out that they are looking for treasure.
   D. Huck is afraid that he will get lost while they are looking for the treasure.

   CCSS.ELA-LITERACY.RL.7.1

Adapted from What Happened to the Dolphins
by Sarah Burkett

Read the article. Then answer the questions that follow.

1. Taylor had returned home to Jacksonville, Florida after a weekend trip to Panama City located in the Florida panhandle. Taylor and his dad adored surfing in the Gulf of Mexico and had a chance to surf in some immense waves. A tropical storm had started brewing, though, so they had to come home sooner than expected, unfortunately. Taylor felt disenchanted about having to go back to school on Monday. His mom was glad that he and his dad had made it home in time for family dinner on Sunday evening, though.

2. While discussing their phenomenal weekend in Panama City, Taylor was suddenly drowned out by the increased decibel of the six o'clock news report.

3. "Breaking news: A considerable amount of Bottlenose dolphins have washed ashore along the Atlantic coast, from New Jersey to Florida. More on this after our break."

4. Taylor's family looked at one another stunned. They had just gone swimming with the dolphins a few weeks back. During Taylor's spring vacation, he and his family took a trip to Discovery Cove in Orlando, Florida. There they met a dolphin named Echo. Echo gave them kisses, played fetch, and took them for a ride on his dorsal fin. In fact, dolphins were Taylor's favorite animal. He hoped to become a marine biologist someday.

5. The newscaster returned from the commercial break. "A government investigation is underway to find the cause for the unusual increase in dolphins washing ashore. Researchers' preliminary results suggest that the red tide found off the coast of Cape Hatteras may have caused this extraordinary rise in dolphin fatalities. We will continue to keep you updated as this story unfolds."

6. Taylor was devastated to learn about the dolphins. In biology class the following day, Taylor asked his instructor, Mr. Kernan, about the dolphin tragedy. Mr. Kernan informed them that close to 150 dolphins were found washed ashore thus far. Taylor asked him about red tides. He explained that red tide was a commonly used term for an algae bloom. He told them that algae blooms occur naturally or as the result of human pollution. Explaining further, he said that typically red tide only affects fish, birds, and shellfish. Interestingly, a decline in the population of these species did not coincide with the decrease in the dolphin population. Furthermore, investigators' initial findings indicated irregularities in the lungs and lymph nodes that were not typically associated with red tide.

7. Later, by the end of the tropical storm season, Taylor learned that 742 dolphin deaths were recorded along the Atlantic coast. Not all dolphins that had died at sea had washed ashore, so it was estimated that approximately 2,500 dolphins perished during the season. This represented more than one half of the inshore population within the affected area.

What Scientists Concluded

8. From June of 1987 to May of 1988, approximately 2,500 bottlenose dolphins died along the eastern coast of the U.S. Results of a scientific investigation concluded that the most likely cause was brevetoxin also known as "red tide." However, this theory was controversial. Although red tide was present in Cape Hatteras, North Carolina in October 1987, no red tide was evident when increased mortality began in New Jersey that June. The lesion found on the dolphins may have been a bacterial or fungal infection. Other government sponsored studies concluded morbillivirus to be the leading cause of death. Research was also conducted to determine if exposure to environmental pollutants such as polychlorinated biphenyls (PCB), dioxins and furans, polyaromatic hydrocarbons and certain heavy metals decreased their resistance to infection. Overall, most findings supported morbillivirus as the primary cause of death.

TIP of the DAY

Paragraphs in information texts include a main idea and supporting evidence.

EXERCISES

1. What does "disenchanted" mean in paragraph 1?

   A. surprised
   B. unclear
   C. excited
   D. unhappy

   CCSS.ELA-LITERACY.RI.7.4

2. What does "drowned out" mean in paragraph 2?

   A. struggling underwater
   B. can no longer be heard
   C. overcome with fear
   D. in disbelief

   CCSS.ELA-LITERACY.RI.7.4

3. According to the article, what causes red tide?

   A. dolphins
   B. surfing
   C. algae
   D. shellfish

   CCSS.ELA-LITERACY.RI.7.3

4. According to the article, what is one reason that the dolphin deaths may not have been caused by the red tide?

   A. Red tide usually only affects fish, birds, and shellfish.
   B. Strong waves in the ocean were more likely the cause.
   C. Dolphins did not come in contact with the red tide.
   D. An oil spill occurred at the same time.

   CCSS.ELA-LITERACY.RI.7.2

5. According to the article, why was 742 not an accurate count of dolphin deaths?

   A. The number did not account for dolphins outside of Florida.
   B. Volunteers were not able to count all of the dolphins.
   C. The number only included the dolphins who washed ashore.
   D. Scientists could only give a rough estimate.

   CCSS.ELA-LITERACY.RI.7.1

6. What caused the lesions found on dolphins?

   A. human pollution
   B. the red tide
   C. morbillivirus
   D. a bacterial or fungal infection

   CCSS.ELA-LITERACY.RI.7.3

Stopping by Woods on a Snowy Evening *by Robert Frost*

Whose woods these are I think I know.
His house is in the village though;
He will not see me stopping here
To watch his woods fill up with snow.

My little horse must think it queer
To stop without a farmhouse near
Between the woods and frozen lake
The darkest evening of the year.

He gives his harness bells a shake
To ask if there is some mistake.
The only other sound's the sweep
Of easy wind and downy flake.

The woods are lovely, dark and deep,
But I have promises to keep,
And miles to go before I sleep,
And miles to go before I sleep.

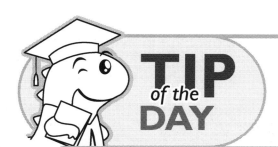

TIP of the DAY

Read poems out loud to help you figure out the rhyme scheme.

EXERCISES

1. Describe the mood found in the poem. Include two details from the poem in your response.

CCSS.ELA-LITERACY.RL.7.3

2. What is the poem's main conflict? Include two details from the poem in your response.

CCSS.ELA-LITERACY.RL.7.2

3. Which rhyme scheme does the author use throughout most of the poem?

A. AABA
B. ABAB
C. AAAB
D. AAAA

CCSS.ELA-LITERACY.RL.7.4

4. Which stanza does not use the rhyme scheme from your answer in question 3?

A. stanza 1
B. stanza 2
C. stanza 3
D. stanza 4

CCSS.ELA-LITERACY.RL.7.4

5. How does the horse's perspective contrast with the speaker's point of view? Select the best answer.

A. The horse finds it strange to have stopped in the woods.
B. The horse dislikes the silence of the woods.
C. The horse does not want to continue the journey.
D. The horse is glad to have stopped in the woods.

CCSS.ELA-LITERACY.RL.7.6

6. The author repeats the final line of the poem. What impact does this have on the poem's meaning? Select the best answer.

A. It stresses that the speaker is exhausted from his travels.
B. It emphasizes the speaker's decision to move on and reach his destination.
C. It indicates that the speaker plans to stay in the village.
D. It reminds the reader why the speaker stopped in the woods.

CCSS.ELA-LITERACY.RL.7.5

WEEK 4

VIDEO EXPLANATIONS ▶

ARGOPREP.COM

FANBOYS

Simple Sentences and Compound Sentences

CCSS.ELA-LITERACY.L.7.1.B

<u>Key Terms</u>

Let's review the parts of a sentence. A sentence must have a subject and a predicate.

Subject: includes the "who" or "what" the sentence is mainly about

Predicate: includes the verb (action or linking)

Complete subjects and predicates can also contain modifiers such as adjectives, adverbs, and phrases.

To add variety to our writing, we can include different kinds of sentences. One way to add variety is to use simple sentences and compound sentences.

What is a simple sentence?

A simple sentence has one subject and one predicate. Another name for a simple sentence is an independent clause.

What is a compound sentence?

A compound sentence has two independent clauses. That means that it has at least two subjects and two predicates.

Compound sentence = independent clause + independent clause

Compound sentences can be joined together in two ways:

- using a semicolon
- using a comma and a coordinating conjunction

We can remember the coordinating conjunctions with the acronym "FANBOYS."

F = for
A = and
N = nor
B = but
O = or
Y = yet
S = so

The type of coordinating conjunction that is used depends on the relationship of ideas between the independent clauses that are being joined together. Use coordinating conjunctions to signal the following relationships between independent clauses.

for: effect and cause (similar to "because")

and: similar ideas

nor: what something is not

but: contrasting ideas

or: choices

yet: stronger contrasting ideas

so: cause and effect

Examples

Simple sentences:

The dog barked loudly.

The baby cried.

We had a holiday party.

Alejandra and Kayla were very excited about the zoo.

Brendan is my best friend.

Compound sentences with semicolons:

The ice cream was melting; *Phil* put it in the freezer.

It was a beautiful day; *our family* went to the park.

Compound sentences with a comma and conjunction:

Jamila got an A on her history test, **for** *she* studied hard.

The pop singer performed on stage, **and** *the crowd* sang along.

Taylor did not make his bed, **nor** did *he* put away his clothes.

I don't like lima beans, **but** *I* do like green beans.

We can watch a movie, **or** *we* can play a game.

Julia tripped on the track, **yet** *she* still won the race.

The car needed more gas, **so** *Kenji and Jackson* stopped at the gas station.

TIP of the DAY

The main linking verbs are forms of «be.» They include be, is, am, was, were, been, being.

38

EXERCISES

Create a compound sentence by joining each pair of simple sentences with a semicolon. Write the compound sentence in the space provided.

1.   The monkey was hungry. The zookeeper gave him a banana.

CCSS.ELA-LITERACY.L.7.1.B

2.   The marathon began. Hundreds of people started running.

CCSS.ELA-LITERACY.L.7.1.B

Create a compound sentence by joining each pair of simple sentences with a comma and the appropriate coordinating conjunction. Write the compound sentence in the space provided.

3.   Becca loves to read. Her favorite books are the *Harry Potter* series.

CCSS.ELA-LITERACY.L.7.1.B

4.   The soccer team lost two games. They practiced harder.

CCSS.ELA-LITERACY.L.7.1.B

5.   He gave the dog a treat. The dog performed a trick.

CCSS.ELA-LITERACY.L.7.1.B

6.   Craig wanted to watch a movie. He had to finish his chores.

CCSS.ELA-LITERACY.L.7.1.B

Complex Sentences

CCSS.ELA-LITERACY.L.7.1.B

Key Terms

What are complex sentences?

Complex sentences have one independent clause and at least one dependent clause.

Complex sentence = independent clause + dependent clause

OR

Complex sentence = dependent clause + independent clause

Let's review independent clauses and dependent clauses.

An independent clause has a subject and a predicate. An independent clause can stand alone as a sentence.

A dependent clause begins with a subordinating conjunction. A dependent clause has a subject and a predicate, but it cannot stand alone as a sentence because it starts with a subordinating conjunction.

To review, here is a list of subordinating conjunctions:

After	How	Unless	Which
Although	If	Until	While
As	Since	When	Who
As if	So that	Whenever	Whom
As though	Than	Where	Whose
Because	That	Wherever	
Before	Though	Whether	

Examples

<u>The cat and the dog became best friends</u>, *even though* **they were different.**

(independent clause + dependent clause)

<u>Marta wants to be an engineer</u> *because* **she loves math.**

(independent clause + dependent clause)

While **we waited in line**, <u>we talked.</u>

(dependent clause + independent clause)

Unless **I save my money**, <u>I can't buy a new car.</u>

(dependent clause + independent clause)

TIP of the DAY

Subordinating conjunctions will help you spot a dependent clause.

40

EXERCISES

Read each sentence. Then select the correct sentence type from the answer choices below.

Read each complex sentence. In the space provided, write the dependent clause.

---

1. The captain steered the boat, and she watched for storm clouds.

   A. simple sentence
   B. compound sentence
   C. complex sentence
   D. interrogative sentence

   CCSS.ELA-LITERACY.L.7.1.B

4. Since the dancer broke his ankle, he watched rehearsals.

   CCSS.ELA-LITERACY.L.7.1.B

---

2. The teacher found the bracelet that Caroline lost.

   A. simple sentence
   B. compound sentence
   C. complex sentence
   D. exclamatory sentence

   CCSS.ELA-LITERACY.L.7.1.B

5. Before you leave, can we talk?

   CCSS.ELA-LITERACY.L.7.1.B

---

3. We ate a lot of pizza slices.

   A. simple sentence
   B. compound sentence
   C. complex sentence
   D. imperative sentence

   CCSS.ELA-LITERACY.L.7.1.B

6. Kate likes watermelon, although she prefers strawberries.

   CCSS.ELA-LITERACY.L.7.1.B

Compound-Complex Sentences

CCSS.ELA-LITERACY.L.7.1.B

<u>Key Terms</u>

What are compound-complex sentences?

Compound-complex sentences contain a compound sentence and a dependent clause.

Compound-complex sentence = independent clause + independent clause + dependent clause

OR

Compound-complex sentence = dependent clause + independent clause + independent clause

Let's review compound sentences and dependent clauses.

Compound sentences have two independent clauses that are joined together with either a semicolon or a comma and coordinating conjunction.

Compound sentence = independent clause + independent clause

The coordinating conjunctions are for, and, nor, but, or, yet, so (FANBOYS).

Dependent clauses have a subject and predicate but begin with a subordinating conjunction.

Some examples of subordinating conjunctions are after, although, because, since, that, though, until, whenever, while.

<u>Examples</u>

While **Valentina ate lunch**, <u>she researched facts</u>, and <u>she brainstormed ideas.</u>

<u>The football team was practicing</u>, but <u>they stopped</u> *because* **the weather was hot.**

Since **tomorrow is a holiday**, <u>they are going shopping</u>, or <u>they are going to a movie.</u>

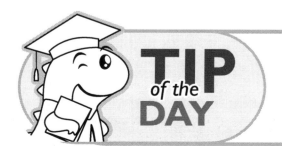

TIP of the **DAY**

Have you memorized the coordinating conjunctions yet? FANBOYS is a mnemonic device. Mnemonic devices help your brain remember facts.

EXERCISES

Read each sentence. Then select the correct sentence type from the answer choices below.

Read each sentence. Select the dependent clause from the answer choices below.

1. Before he ran three miles, Mario ate a snack.

    A. simple sentence
    B. compound sentence
    C. complex sentence
    D. compound-complex sentence

    CCSS.ELA-LITERACY.L.7.1.B

4. Even though she likes scary movies, the movie was boring, and she fell asleep.

    A. Even though she likes scary movies
    B. likes scary movies
    C. the movie was boring
    D. she fell asleep

    CCSS.ELA-LITERACY.L.7.1.B

2. While the teacher was instructing, Lisa listened, and she took notes.

    A. simple sentence
    B. compound sentence
    C. complex sentence
    D. compound-complex sentence

    CCSS.ELA-LITERACY.L.7.1.B

5. Because his lunch was cold, Dave warmed it in the microwave, but then it was too hot.

    A. Because his lunch was cold
    B. Dave warmed it
    C. Dave warmed it in the microwave
    D. then it was too hot

    CCSS.ELA-LITERACY.L.7.1.B

3. It was very cold, yet the sun was shining.

    A. simple sentence
    B. compound sentence
    C. complex sentence
    D. compound-complex sentence

    CCSS.ELA-LITERACY.L.7.1.B

6. We can work on math, or we can work on social studies, before we go to lunch.

    A. We can work on math
    B. we can work on social studies
    C. or we can
    D. before we go to lunch

    CCSS.ELA-LITERACY.L.7.1.B

WEEK 5

:VIDEO
EXPLANATIONS

ARGOPREP.COM

Excerpt of Little Women
by Louisa May Alcott

1. "Christmas won't be Christmas without any presents," grumbled Jo, lying on the rug.

2. "It's so dreadful to be poor!" sighed Meg, looking down at her old dress.

3. "I don't think it's fair for some girls to have plenty of pretty things, and other girls nothing at all," added little Amy, with an injured sniff.

4. "We've got Father and Mother, and each other," said Beth contentedly from her corner.

5. The four young faces on which the firelight shone brightened at the cheerful words, but darkened again as Jo said sadly, "We haven't got Father, and shall not have him for a long time." She didn't say "perhaps never," but each silently added it, thinking of Father far away, where the fighting was.

6. Nobody spoke for a minute; then Meg said in an altered tone, "You know the reason Mother proposed not having any presents this Christmas was because it is going to be a hard winter for everyone; and she thinks we ought not to spend money for pleasure, when our men are suffering so in the army. We can't do much, but we can make our little sacrifices, and ought to do it gladly. But I am afraid I don't," and Meg shook her head, as she thought regretfully of all the pretty things she wanted.

7. "But I don't think the little we should spend would do any good. We've each got a dollar, and the army wouldn't be much helped by our giving that. I agree not to expect anything from Mother or you, but I do want to buy Undine and Sintram for myself. I've wanted it so long," said Jo, who was a bookworm.

8. "I planned to spend mine in new music," said Beth, with a little sigh, which no one heard but the hearth brush and kettle holder.

9. "I shall get a nice box of Faber's drawing pencils. I really need them," said Amy decidedly.

10. "Mother didn't say anything about our money, and she won't wish us to give up everything. Let's each buy what we want, and have a little fun. I'm sure we work hard enough to earn it," cried Jo, examining the heels of her shoes in a gentlemanly manner.

11. "I know I do — teaching those tiresome children nearly all day, when I'm longing to enjoy myself at home," began Meg, in the complaining tone again.

12. "You don't have half such a hard time as I do," said Jo. "How would you like to be shut up for hours with a nervous, fussy old lady, who keeps you trotting, is never satisfied, and worries you till you're ready to fly out the window or cry?"

13. "It's naughty to fret, but I do think washing dishes and keeping things tidy is the worst work in the world. It makes me cross, and my hands get so stiff, I can't practice well at all." And Beth looked at her rough hands with a sigh that any one could hear that time.

14. "I don't believe any of you suffer as I do," cried Amy, "for you don't have to go to school with impertinent girls, who plague you if you don't know your lessons, and laugh at your dresses, and label your father if he isn't rich, and insult you when your nose isn't nice."

15. "If you mean libel, I'd say so, and not talk about labels, as if Papa was a pickle bottle," advised Jo, laughing.

16. "I know what I mean, and you needn't be statirical about it. It's proper to use good words, and improve your vocabilary," returned Amy, with dignity.

17. "Don't peck at one another, children. Don't you wish we had the money Papa lost when we were little, Jo? Dear me! How happy and good we'd be, if we had no worries!" said Meg, who could remember better times.

18. "You said the other day you thought we were a deal happier than the King children, for they were fighting and fretting all the time, in spite of their money."

19. "So I did, Beth. Well, I think we are. For though we do have to work, we make fun of ourselves, and are a pretty jolly set, as Jo would say."

20. "Jo does use such slang words!" observed Amy, with a reproving look at the long figure stretched on the rug.

21. Jo immediately sat up, put her hands in her pockets, and began to whistle.

22. "Don't, Jo. It's so boyish!"

23. "That's why I do it."

24. "I detest rude, unladylike girls!"

25. "I hate affected, niminy-piminy chits!"

26. "Birds in their little nests agree," sang Beth, the peacemaker, with such a funny face that both sharp voices softened to a laugh, and the "pecking" ended for that time.

27. "Really, girls, you are both to be blamed," said Meg, beginning to lecture in her elder-sister fashion. "You are old enough to leave off boyish tricks, and to behave better, Josephine. It didn't matter so much when you were a little girl, but now you are so tall, and turn up your hair, you should remember that you are a young lady."

28. "I'm not! And if turning up my hair makes me one, I'll wear it in two tails till I'm twenty," cried Jo, pulling off her net, and shaking down a chestnut mane. "I hate to think I've got to grow up, and be Miss March, and wear long gowns, and look as prim as a China Aster! It's bad enough to be a girl, anyway, when I like boy's games and work and manners! I can't get over my disappointment in not being a boy. And it's worse than ever now, for I'm dying to go and fight with Papa. And I can only stay home and knit, like a poky old woman!"

29. And Jo shook the blue army sock till the needles rattled like castanets, and her ball bounded across the room.

30. "Poor Jo! It's too bad, but it can't be helped. So you must try to be contented with making your name boyish, and playing brother to us girls," said Beth, stroking the rough head with a hand that all the dish washing and dusting in the world could not make ungentle in its touch.

31. "As for you, Amy," continued Meg, "you are altogether too particular and prim. Your airs are funny now, but you'll grow up an affected little goose, if you don't take care. I like your nice manners and refined ways of speaking, when you don't try to be elegant. But your absurd words are as bad as Jo's slang."

32. "If Jo is a tomboy and Amy a goose, what am I, please?" asked Beth, ready to share the lecture.

33. "You're a dear, and nothing else," answered Meg warmly, and no one contradicted her, for the 'Mouse' was the pet of the family.

TIP
of the
DAY

*There are several film adaptations of **Little Women** that you can watch and compare to the book.*

1. In paragraph 2, "dreadful" most likely means

    A. confusing
    B. wonderful
    C. unkind
    D. horrible

    CCSS.ELA-LITERACY.RL.7.4

2. Which two words in paragraphs 1 and 2 help support the meaning of "dreadful"?

    A. Christmas, presents
    B. grumbled, sighed
    C. old, dress
    D. lying, looking

    CCSS.ELA-LITERACY.RL.7.1

3. Based on paragraphs 5 and 6, it can be determined that the setting takes place during

    A. an important presidential election
    B. a time of war
    C. a happy celebration
    D. a search for a missing person

    CCSS.ELA-LITERACY.RL.7.3

4. Which paragraph best emphasizes a main idea found in paragraphs 14-16?

    A. paragraph 20
    B. paragraph 21
    C. paragraph 31
    D. paragraph 32

    CCSS.ELA-LITERACY.RL.7.6

5. Which statement best represents Jo's point of view in the story?

    A. Jo does not want to behave the way society expects her to behave.
    B. Jo believes that her sisters should improve their vocabulary.
    C. Jo wishes that her family had more money.
    D. Jo does not enjoy taking care of her younger sisters.

    CCSS.ELA-LITERACY.RL.7.6

6. Which sentence from the story supports your answer from question 5?

    A. "If you mean libel, I'd say so, and not talk about labels, as if Papa was a pickle bottle," advised Jo, laughing.
    B. "You are old enough to leave off boyish tricks, and to behave better, Josephine."
    C. "I hate to think I've got to grow up, and be Miss March, and wear long gowns, and look as prim as a China Aster!"
    D. And Jo shook the blue army sock till the needles rattled like castanets, and her ball bounded across the room.

    CCSS.ELA-LITERACY.RL.7.1

Rules for Court Circular
by Lewis Carroll

Lewis Carroll, the author of Alice's Adventures in Wonderland, *was also a mathematician and puzzle creator. He worked on a book called* Games and Puzzles, *although he did not finish writing it before he died. The following passage explains a game that Carroll created. Read the instructions for the game and then answer the questions that follow.*

(A New Game of Cards for Two or More Players)

SECTION I. (For Two Players)

I

CUT for precedence. Highest is `first-hand'; lowest `dealer'. Dealer gives 6 cards to each, one by one, beginning with first-hand, and turns up the 13th, which is called the `Lead'. It is convenient that the same player should be dealer for the whole of each game.

II

First-hand then plays a card; then the other player, and so on, until 6 cards have been played, when the trick is complete, and he who can make (out of the 3 cards he has played, with or without the Lead), the best `Line', wins it.

III

A `Line' consists of 2, or all 3, of the cards put down by either player, with or without the Lead. In making a Line, it does not matter in what order the 3 cards have been put down. Lines rank as follows:

1. 3, or 4, CARDS, (LEAD *included*)

Trio — i.e. 3 of a sort, (e.g. 3 Kings, or 3 Nines.)
Sequence — i.e. 3, or 4, in Sequence, (e.g. Eight, Nine, Ten, Knave.)
Sympathy — i.e. 3, or 4, Hearts.
Court — i.e. 3, or 4, Court-cards, (if 4, it is called Court Circular.)
In this Class a Line of 4 cards beats a *similar* Line of 3. The Lead must not be counted in the middle of a Sequence.

2. 3 CARDS, (LEAD *excluded*)

Names as above.
In making a Sequence, the Ace may be counted either with King, Queen, or with Two, Three.

3. 2 CARDS, (LEAD *excluded*)

Pair — i.e. 2 of a sort.
Valentine — i.e. 2 Hearts.
Etiquette — i.e. 2 Court-cards.

IV

If both have made Lines of the same kind, he whose Line contains the best card wins the trick; and if neither has made a Line, he who has played the best card wins it. Cards rank as follows:

1. Hearts.
2. The rest of the pack, in order Aces, Kings, etc.

If no Hearts have been played, and the highest cards on each side are equal, (e.g. if each have played an Ace), they rank in the order Diamonds, Clubs, Spades.

V

The winner of a trick chooses, as Lead for the next trick, any one of the cards on the table, except the old Lead; he then takes the rest, turning them face upwards, if he is first-hand, but if not, face downwards; and he becomes first-hand for the next trick.

VI

The dealer then gives cards to each, one by one, beginning with first-hand, until each hand is made up again to 6 cards.

TIP of the DAY

Informational texts come in many forms, including game instructions. The next time you play a board game, use the same reading strategies for understanding the instructions.

EXERCISES

1. Which card is considered the Lead?

   A. the first
   B. the sixth
   C. the twelfth
   D. the thirteenth

2. What does "first-hand" mean as it is used in the game instructions?

   A. the card that is facing down
   B. the card that is facing up
   C. the player who takes a turn first
   D. the card dealer

3. How does a player win the game? Select the best answer.

   A. playing three cards
   B. playing the best line
   C. playing a Heart
   D. playing a Diamond, Club, and Spade

4. What is the purpose of section III in the game instructions?

   A. It explains the role of each player.
   B. It details how the dealer distributes the cards.
   C. It explains what to do if two players win.
   D. It provides detailed instructions on card rank.

5. Which text structure did Carroll use overall?

   A. compare and contrast
   B. problem and solution
   C. chronological order
   D. sequential order

6. Which statement below would be included in a summary of the game instructions? Select the best answer.

   A. In every round, each player receives six cards.
   B. An example of a Trio is three eight cards.
   C. A Valentine is two hearts.
   D. There are at least two first-hands.

WEEK 5 : FRIDAY

Adapted from Tubas
by Catherine Schmidt-Jones

Read the passage. Then answer the questions that follow.

Introduction

The tuba is the largest, lowest-sounding instrument in the brass section of the Western orchestra. It is a cup-mouthpiece aerophone with a conical bore.

The Instrument

Tubas come in many different lengths (9 feet, 12, 14, 16, or more) and bore sizes; most are bass or contrabass instruments. Common instruments include E flat, F, and EEflat bass tubas and BBflat and CC contrabass tubas (which have an even deeper sound than the bass instruments). Preferences for specific tuba sizes vary from one country to another. Also, E flat and B flat are more useful in bands, which tend to play in flat keys; F and C are more common in orchestras. None of these are transposing instruments.

Most instruments that are named by a particular note (like B flat clarinet) are transposing instruments. In the case of tubas, and a few other instruments, the name simply tells you the fundamental of the instrument, that is, the note that the no-valves harmonic series of the instrument is based on.

Many different types and sizes of baritone and tenor tubas have also been made. The ones that are in common use today are usually not called tubas, although they are still part of the tuba family.

Tubas can have from three to six valves. For most of the smaller brass instruments (trumpets, horns, and so on), three valves is enough to get all the notes reasonably in tune. The large size of tubas makes it more difficult to find a length of tubing that will lower the pitch of both high harmonics and low harmonics by the same amount (one half step, or one whole step, for example). The extra valves give the tubas plenty of alternative fingerings, so that both high and low notes can be played in tune. They also make it possible to get more notes in the lowest octave of the instrument.

The sousaphone is a modern instrument, with three or four valves. It is designed to be carried over a shoulder, with the tubing in a circle around the player, who can easily stand or march with the instrument. Its bell points forward. (I am told that the first one, made in 1898, had a bell pointing straight up. I hope they never had to march in the rain with that one!) To make them even easier to carry, some sousaphones are made of fiberglass rather than metal. Most sousaphones are BBflat, although other sizes, such as Eflat are made.

There are also some marching tubas that are wrapped in the more standard oblong shape, designed to be carried on the shoulder. Most tubas, however, are wrapped in an oblong shape designed to be held (or rested) in front of a seated player. The bell may point straight up, or up and forward.

The Wagner tuba is a cross between a horn and a tuba. It is usually played by horn players (not tuba players) using horn-type mouthpieces, and is always used in sets of four (two tenors and two basses). It is rarely called for outside of the music of Wagner, and Wagner tuba parts these days are often played by other, more common instruments.

History

The tuba may be considered the youngest instrument normally found in the orchestra. The various strings and percussion are easily centuries old. The various woodwinds, though greatly improved in the nineteenth century, also have older pedigrees. Even among the brass, there were valveless trumpets and horns for centuries, and the slide trombone has lasted nearly unchanged since medieval times. But a large valveless brass instrument is of very limited use, so European instrument makers didn't really experiment with large brass until high-quality valves were available. The tuba was invented by Wilhelm Wieprecht, a bandmaster and trombone player in Berlin who patented the design in 1835. He wanted a "true contrabass wind instrument". Once the tuba did become common, it replaced both the serpent (a large wooden instrument) and the ophicleide (a large keyed bugle) completely, and both of those instruments died out.

Music Using the Tuba

The function of the tuba most of the time is to play bass lines in full-orchestra or full-brass sections of the music, so it can be difficult to distinguish the tuba as a separate instrument, and orchestral music before the late 1800's does not have tubas at all. Tubas are more numerous in bands than in orchestras; you may want to search for music for brass bands, military bands, marching bands, or even wind ensembles. There are also some (late nineteenth and twentieth century) orchestral works in which the tubas are noticeable. Some brass chamber music also includes a tuba. You should be able to find recordings of some of the following pieces, in which the tubas are unusually easy to hear:

- Holst's Suite in E flat (for band)
- Vaughan Williams' Folk Song Suite (for band)
- Sousa's Semper Fidelis and El Capitan marches (for band)
- Josef Franz Wagner's Under the Double Eagle (for band)
- Holst's The Planets, especially "Mars" and "Uranus"
- Rimsky-Korsakov's orchestration of Moussorgsky's Night on Bare Mountain (also translated as Night on Bald Mountain)
- Kleinsinger's "Tubby the Tuba" is a work for solo tuba to be performed for children.

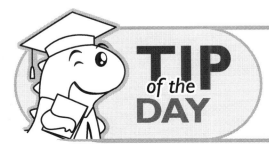

TIP of the DAY

A strategy for understanding informational texts is to underline or highlight interesting facts and to write questions you have about the text.

1. Which type of tubas are most useful in bands? Include two details from the passage in your response.

   _____

   _____

   _____

   _____

   CCSS.ELA-LITERACY.RI.7.1

2. Why do tubas have more valves than other brass instruments? Include two details from the passage in your response.

   _____

   _____

   _____

   _____

   CCSS.ELA-LITERACY.RI.7.1

3. How does a sousaphone differ from most other tubas?

   A. It is used in harmony with trumpets.
   B. It was used primarily in medieval times.
   C. It plays lower notes than other tubas.
   D. Its shape and weight allows the player to carry it.

   CCSS.ELA-LITERACY.RI.7.4

4. Which text structure does the author use in the passage?

   A. description
   B. cause and effect
   C. sequential order
   D. compare and contrast

   CCSS.ELA-LITERACY.RI.7.5

5. Which statement is a central idea from the passage?

   A. The tuba was patented in 1835.
   B. The tuba is the largest brass instrument.
   C. The bell of tuba may point straight up, or up and forward.
   D. Brass chamber music includes a tuba.

   CCSS.ELA-LITERACY.RI.7.2

6. Why does the author include the bulleted list at the end of the passage?

   A. It states information that contrasts from the rest of the paragraph.
   B. It provides a transition between two central ideas.
   C. It allows information to be clearly organized for the reader.
   D. It summarizes the previous paragraphs.

   CCSS.ELA-LITERACY.RI.7.5

WEEK 6

VIDEO
EXPLANATIONS

ARGOPREP.COM

Capitalization Practice

CCSS.ELA-LITERACY.L.7.2

<u>Key Terms and Examples</u>

Do you remember when you should capitalize a word? Let's review the rules for capitalization.

Sentences

Be sure to capitalize the first letter of the first word in a sentence.

<u>Example</u>: **M**y dog is the cutest in the world. **S**he loves to snuggle and play in the park.

Proper Nouns

Proper nouns—the names of people, places, and things — must be capitalized.

<u>Example</u>: Someday I would like to visit the **G**rand **C**anyon.

Proun "I"

The pronoun "I" is always capitalized.

<u>Example</u>: Maria and I have been best friends since first grade.

Title of Works

The title of works such as books, films, short stories, poems, etc. should be capitalized. The main words in the title will be capitalized, but minor words such as "a," "an," "the," and prepositions such as "in," "of," "on" do not need to be capitalized.

<u>Example</u>: In English class we are reading *To Kill a Mockingbird*.

Dialogue or a Quote

The first letter that begins a character's dialogue should be capitalized, even if the dialogue begins in the middle of a sentence.

<u>Example</u>: The nurse told the patient, "**Y**ou have been in an accident, but we are here to help you."

When quoting someone, the first letter that begins the quote should also be capitalized, even if the quote begins in the middle of a sentence.

<u>Example</u>: The astronaut told journalists, "**T**here are many planets in our galaxy yet to be discovered."

Titles of People and Occupations

The first letter of titles such as Mr., Mrs, Dr., etc. should be capitalized.

<u>Example</u>: **D**r. Othello is an excellent surgeon.

WEEK 6 : MONDAY

When addressing a person by their occupation (such as when addressing a president, manager, mayor), capitalize their title.

Example: Did you know that **P**resident Abraham Lincoln was born in Illinois?

Salutation of a Letter

A salutation is how you address the person or company to whom you are writing the letter. Begin the first letter.

Example: **D**ear Mrs. Jackson,
I am writing in regards to the software engineer position.

Closing of a Letter

When closing a letter, capitalize the first letter of the word or phrase that you use.

Example: **Y**ours truly,
Joanna Mills

TIP
of the
DAY

When writing a letter to someone you know, use a comma after the salutation. When writing a formal letter to a company or business person, use a colon after the salutation.

EXERCISES

Read each selection. Then choose the answer which corrects any errors in capitalization.

1. michelle is reading a book called *little women*.

    A. Michelle is reading a book called *little women*.
    B. Michelle is Reading a book called *little women*.
    C. Michelle is reading a Book called *little Women*.
    D. Michelle is reading a book called *Little Women*.

CCSS.ELA-LITERACY.L.7.2

2. People in the town respect mayor delilah brown.

    A. People in the town Respect mayor delilah brown.
    B. People in the town respect mayor delilah brown.
    C. People in the town respect Mayor Delilah Brown.
    D. People in the town respect mayor Delilah Brown.

CCSS.ELA-LITERACY.L.7.2

3. The rocky mountains cover part of colorado.

    A. The Rocky Mountains cover part of Colorado.
    B. The Rocky Mountains cover part of colorado.
    C. The rocky mountains cover part of Colorado.
    D. The Rocky mountains cover part of colorado.

CCSS.ELA-LITERACY.L.7.2

Rewrite each sentence to correct any errors in capitalization.

4. The little girl said, "my name is laura."

CCSS.ELA-LITERACY.L.7.2

EXERCISES

5. Have you ever visited the atlantic ocean?

CCSS.ELA-LITERACY.L.7.2

6. john and i sit next to each other in class.

CCSS.ELA-LITERACY.L.7.2

NOTES

WEEK 6 : WEDNESDAY

Introductory Words, Phrases, and Clauses

CCSS.ELA-LITERACY.L.7.2

Key Terms

What does the word "introductory" mean?

Introductory means that a word, phrase, or clause starts a sentence. We use commas after introductory words, phrases, and clauses.

Introductory Words

When including an introductory word at the beginning of the sentence, include a comma after the word. The comma acts as a pause before the main part of the sentence.

Examples

Yes, I would like a chocolate chip cookie.
No, I do not understand.
Well, I'm not sure that I like that dress.

Introductory Phrases

When an introductory infinitive phrase begins a sentence, we add a comma after the phrase.

Example:

To fly to France, we have to stop in New York first.

When an introductory prepositional phrase is longer than four words, we add a comma after the phrase. If the prepositional phrase is shorter, adding a comma is optional.

Example:

After P.E. and science class, I go to math class.

Introductory Dependent Clauses

When a dependent clause begins a sentence, we add a comma after the clause. This helps separate it from the main independent clause.

Example:

Before we run laps, we have to stretch.

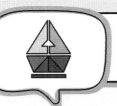

EXERCISES

Rewrite each sentence below to correct the error in punctuation.

1. During the movie we ate popcorn and candy.

CCSS.ELA-LITERACY.L.7.2

2. Yes there was a supercontinent called Pangea.

CCSS.ELA-LITERACY.L.7.2

3. To make a cake we need flour and eggs.

CCSS.ELA-LITERACY.L.7.2

4. Because she was allergic she had to stay away from the dog.

CCSS.ELA-LITERACY.L.7.2

5. When Claire hit the ball she ran to first base.

CCSS.ELA-LITERACY.L.7.2

6. If you like chocolate you'll love this pie.

CCSS.ELA-LITERACY.L.7.2

Coordinating Adjectives and Commas

CCSS.ELA-LITERACY.L.7.2.A

Key Terms

Let's review adjectives.

Adjectives are words that modify or describe nouns or pronouns. They answer the questions:

- What kind?
- How many?
- Which one(s)?
- Whose?

What are coordinate adjectives?

Coordinate adjectives appear in sequence or list, one adjective after another. All of the coordinate adjectives that are listed modify the same noun. In fact, the adjectives can be written in any order because they all describe the same noun.

Coordinate adjectives are independent of one another and hold the same weight.

When listing coordinate adjectives, we separate them with commas. We can also separate them with the word "and."

What are cumulative adjectives?

Cumulative adjectives are listed after a noun, but they describe the noun and then a combination of the next adjective along with the noun.

Cumulative adjectives don't need any commas between them. We don't add the word "and" in between cumulative adjectives either.

Examples

Coordinate adjectives:

I found a rusted, broken bicycle in the basement.
I found a rusted and broken bicycle in the basement.

The painting was enormous, colorful.
The painting was enormous and colorful.

Cumulative adjectives:

The three pink pigs loved rolling in the mud.
("The three and pink pigs …" does not work.)

Dad made fluffy blueberry pancakes.
("…fluffy and blueberry pancakes" does not work.)

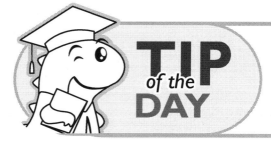

TIP of the DAY

Add adjectives to your own writing to be descriptive and clear about your topic.

EXERCISES

Read each sentence. Identify whether each sentence contains coordinate adjectives or cumulative adjectives. Write your answer in the space provided.

Read each sentence. Select the answer containing the correct punctuation placement.

1. My mom made a big chocolate cake for my birthday.

_____

_____

CCSS.ELA-LITERACY.L.7.2.A

2. Jamie is a smart, funny girl.

_____

_____

CCSS.ELA-LITERACY.L.7.2.A

3. The soft, furry rabbit likes to nap in the grass.

_____

_____

_____

CCSS.ELA-LITERACY.L.7.2.A

4. The ripe squishy peach needs to be eaten.

   A. The ripe, squishy, peach needs to be eaten.
   B. The ripe, squishy peach needs to be eaten.
   C. The ripe squishy peach, needs to be eaten.
   D. Answer is correct as is.

CCSS.ELA-LITERACY.L.7.2.A

5. It was a snowy cold winter.

   A. It was a snowy, cold winter.
   B. It was a snowy, cold, winter.
   C. It was a, snowy cold winter.
   D. Answer is correct as is.

CCSS.ELA-LITERACY.L.7.2.A

6. The tall skinny boy is on the basketball team.

   A. The tall skinny, boy is on the basketball team.
   B. The tall skinny boy is on the basketball, team.
   C. The tall, skinny boy is on the basketball team.
   D. Answer is correct as is.

CCSS.ELA-LITERACY.L.7.2.A

WEEK 7

: **VIDEO**
• **EXPLANATIONS** ▶

A Dream within a Dream *by Edgar Allan Poe*

Take this kiss upon the brow!
And, in parting from you now,
Thus much let me avow —
You are not wrong, who deem
That my days have been a dream;
Yet if hope has flown away
In a night, or in a day,
In a vision, or in none,
Is it therefore the less gone?
All that we see or seem
Is but a dream within a dream.

I stand amid the roar
Of a surf-tormented shore,
And I hold within my hand
Grains of the golden sand —
How few! yet how they creep
Through my fingers to the deep,
While I weep — while I weep!
O God! Can I not grasp
Them with a tighter clasp?
O God! can I not save
One from the pitiless wave?
Is all that we see or seem
But a dream within a dream?

TIP *of the* DAY

Edgar Allan Poe is well-known for his mysterious (or even scary) poems and short stories.

EXERCISES

1. What is the rhyme scheme used in stanza 1?

   A. ababababccd
   B. abcdefabcdef
   C. aaabbccddee
   D. aaabbccddbb

   CCSS.ELA-LITERACY.RL.7.4

2. Based on stanza 2, where is the speaker?

   A. in a house
   B. on a beach
   C. on a mountaintop
   D. in a field

   CCSS.ELA-LITERACY.RL.7.2

3. What type of literary device does the author employ in the following lines?

   > I stand amid the roar
   > Of a surf-tormented shore,
   > And I hold within my hand
   > Grains of the golden sand —

   A. onomatopoeia
   B. imagery
   C. simile
   D. hyperbole

   CCSS.ELA-LITERACY.RL.7.4

4. What does the author use to create the literary device? Select the best answer.

   A. exaggeration
   B. comparison
   C. sensory details
   D. contrast

   CCSS.ELA-LITERACY.RL.7.4

5. What impact does this literary device have on the poem's meaning? Select the best answer.

   A. It communicates where the narrator is traveling.
   B. It helps clarify the narrator's relationship with nature.
   C. It provides information about the narrator's background.
   D. It helps express the narrator's sadness.

   CCSS.ELA-LITERACY.RL.7.4

6. What is a theme found in the poem?

   A. Life does not last forever.
   B. Journeys can be long.
   C. Dreams are hard to remember.
   D. Everyone has dreams in life.

   CCSS.ELA-LITERACY.RL.7.2

Introduction

1. The didjeridu (also spelled didjeridoo or didgeridoo) is a musical instrument that is an important part of the traditions of the Aboriginal people of northern Australia. It is a simple aerophone consisting of a long hollow tube shaped to create a mouthpiece at one end. The instrument is usually made of wood, but is considered to be in the brass family (sometimes called the "lip-reed" or "cup-mouthpiece" family) because, as with all "brass" instruments, its sound is created by buzzing the lips against the rim of the mouthpiece.

The Instrument

2. A didjeridu made in the traditional way is always a unique work of art, reflecting both its original natural shape and the musical and visual tastes of those who shaped and decorated it.

3. The typical didjeridu consists simply of a tube with a mouthpiece at one end. The tube is traditionally made from a termite-hollowed eucalyptus tree. (Sometimes a branch that is large enough and straight enough can be found, but more commonly, it is the trunk of a young tree.) When a hollow tree of the right size is found, the bark is removed, and its innards may be further hollowed and shaped to produce a better sound. The outside of the instrument may be painted and/or varnished. Some modern instruments are made of other materials, such as bamboo or other kinds of wood.

4. The traditional instrument has no fingering holes, keys, valves, or slides. Some modern didjeridus have a slide construction similar to a trombone, or even saxophone-style keys that allow a melody to be played, but these are unusual.

5. The typical didjeridu is between one and two meters in length, but some are longer than three meters. As with any wind instrument, larger and longer didjeridus produce lower sounds than smaller instruments. Some instruments have a more conical shape and some are more cylindrical, and this also affects the sound of the instrument.

The rim of one end of the tube is altered slightly to form the mouthpiece. If one end of a didjeridu is already the right size and shape to accommodate the lips, simply smoothing it out to make it comfortable is often enough to create a mouthpiece. In many instruments, though, a layer of beeswax is added to the rim. The consistency of the beeswax, which becomes malleable at warm temperatures, makes it ideal for shaping a comfortable, efficient mouthpiece. The diameter and thickness of the rim are similar to the rim of the mouthpiece of a low brass instrument such as the tuba or trombone, and the technique for getting a sound is quite similar. In this family of instruments, the sound is created by "buzzing" the lips inside the mouthpiece rim.

WEEK 7 : WEDNESDAY

History and Culture

6. The didjeridu originated in northern Australia. In fact, it can be considered a family of instruments, since several different native groups have a specific local version of the instrument, with a local name. (Aboriginal Australians come from a variety of related cultures, with different languages and customs, not a single uniform culture.) A didjeridu made by the Yolngu people, for example, is a yidaki. The term didjeridu is apparently a Western coinage, and is a generic name covering all Australian instruments of this type.
It is an ancient instrument, in the same category as other traditional lip-reed wind instruments, made from a variety of materials, from branches to animal horns to conch shells, and found in many cultures around the world. Archaeological records show the didjeridu is at least 1500 years old, and it may be much older than that, possibly even one of the oldest wind instruments ever invented anywhere.

7. Didjeridu traditions center in Arnhem Land, the largest Aboriginal freehold area in Australia. It is located at the "top end" of Australia's Northern Territory (its north central state). There are actually three distinct musical traditions in this area, which include different didjeridu playing styles. For example, in eastern Arnhem land, players tend to alternate rapidly between the two easily-available pitches; in the central area the alternation between the two is slower, and players in the Western part of the area tend to play only the fundamental, deriving interest from variation in timbre and other techniques.

8. Some musical events in Australian Aboriginal communities have intense religious and cultural significance and are not open to the public; specific instruments and players are called for on these occasions. Other events are open-to-the-public performances. Although playing the didjeridu is traditionally considered a man's job, and Aboriginal people may consider a didjeridu-playing woman to be shocking or humorous (in the same way that an American might consider it shocking or humorous to see a man wearing a dress), there are no particular rules against outsiders playing the instrument.

9. In fact, in recent times, the world music movement has created widespread interest in non-Western musical traditions, including instruments such as the didjeridu, which now are sometimes included in cross-tradition ensembles. As of this writing the band Yothu Yindi has had the greatest impact in introducing the didjeridu to the rest of the world. Most Aboriginal Australians have no problem with the idea of the instrument being used in non-traditional ways, but some are troubled by the mass production of poorer-quality, inauthentic instruments.

TIP of the DAY

Informational texts have overall central ideas, and each paragraph has a central idea. Identifying these will help you better understand the text.

EXERCISES

1. Despite being made of wood, what is surprising about the didjeridu?

   A. It is a modern instrument.
   B. It is smaller than a saxophone.
   C. It is part of the brass family.
   D. It is a string instrument.

   CCSS.ELA-LITERACY.RI.7.1

2. What is the purpose of paragraph 2? Select the best answer.

   A. It states the central idea.
   B. It provides support for the introductory paragraph.
   C. It explains the cultural importance of the instrument.
   D. It describes the origin of the name "didjeridu."

   CCSS.ELA-LITERACY.RI.7.5

3. What is true of instruments that produce lower sounds?

   A. The shorter the instrument, the lower the sound that it produces.
   B. The wider the instrument, the lower the sound that it produces.
   C. The narrower the instrument, the lower the sound that it produces.
   D. The longer the instrument, the lower the sound that it produces.

   CCSS.ELA-LITERACY.RI.7.1

4. What does "malleable" mean as it is used in paragraph 5? Select the best answer.

   A. able to be changed into liquid
   B. hard and unable to move
   C. cold and frozen
   D. flexible and able to be formed

   CCSS.ELA-LITERACY.RI.7.4

5. Which word contrasts with the meaning of uniform as it is used in paragraph 6?

   A. different
   B. same
   C. creative
   D. familiar

   CCSS.ELA-LITERACY.RI.7.4

6. Which statement best summarizes paragraph 9?

   A. Yothu Yindi is a popular band in Australia and plays the didjeridu.
   B. Many people around the world are interested in non-Western instruments, including the didjeridu.
   C. The didjeridu is sometimes now used in modern music ensembles.
   D. The didjeridu has become popular outside of Australia, but Aboriginals are upset that some companies are making poor-quality instruments.

   CCSS.ELA-LITERACY.RI.7.2

WEEK 7 : FRIDAY

The Invisible Man *by H.G. Wells*

1. The stranger came early in February, one wintry day, through a biting wind and a driving snow, the last snowfall of the year, over the down, walking as it seemed from Bramblehurst railway station, and carrying a little black portmanteau in his thickly gloved hand. He was wrapped up from head to foot, and the brim of his soft felt hat hid every inch of his face but the shiny tip of his nose; the snow had piled itself against his shoulders and chest, and added a white crest to the burden he carried. He staggered into the Coach and Horses, more dead than alive as it seemed, and flung his portmanteau down. "A fire," he cried, "in the name of human charity! A room and a fire!" He stamped and shook the snow from off himself in the bar, and followed Mrs. Hall into her guest parlour to strike his bargain. And with that much introduction, that and a ready acquiescence to terms and a couple of sovereigns flung upon the table, he took up his quarters in the inn.

2. Mrs. Hall lit the fire and left him there while she went to prepare him a meal with her own hands. A guest to stop in the town in the wintertime was an unheard-of piece of luck, let alone a guest who was no "haggler," and she was resolved to show herself worthy of her good fortune. As soon as the bacon was well under way, and Millie, her lymphatic aid, had been brisked up a bit by a few deftly chosen expressions of contempt, she carried the cloth, plates, and glasses into the parlour and began to lay them with the utmost eclat. Although the fire was burning up briskly, she was surprised to see that her visitor still wore his hat and coat, standing with his back to her and staring out of the window at the falling snow in the yard. His gloved hands were clasped behind him, and he seemed to be lost in thought. She noticed that the melted snow that still sprinkled his shoulders dropped upon her carpet. "Can I take your hat and coat, sir," she said, "and give them a good dry in the kitchen?"

3. "No," he said without turning.

4. She was not sure she had heard him, and was about to repeat her question.

5. He turned his head and looked at her over his shoulder. "I prefer to keep them on," he said with emphasis, and she noticed that he wore big blue spectacles with sidelights, and had a bushy side-whisker over his coat-collar that completely hid his cheeks and face.

6. "Very well, sir," she said. "As you like. In a bit the room will be warmer."

7. He made no answer, and had turned his face away from her again, and Mrs. Hall, feeling that her conversational advances were ill-timed, laid the rest of the table things in a quick staccato and whisked out of the room. When she returned he was still standing there, like a man of stone, his back hunched, his collar turned up, his dripping hat-brim turned down, hiding his face and ears completely. She put down the eggs and bacon with considerable emphasis, and called rather than said to him, "Your lunch is served, sir."

8. "Thank you," he said at the same time, and did not stir until she was closing the door. Then he swung round and approached the table with a certain eager quickness.

9. As she went behind the bar to the kitchen she heard a sound repeated at regular intervals. Chirk, chirk, chirk, it went, the sound of a spoon being rapidly whisked round a basin. "That girl!" she said. "There! I clean forgot it. It's her being so long!" And while she herself finished mixing the mustard, she gave Millie a few verbal stabs for her excessive slowness. She had cooked the ham and eggs, laid the table, and done everything, while Millie (help indeed!) had only succeeded in delaying the mustard. And him a new guest and wanting to stay! Then she filled the mustard pot, and, putting it with a certain stateliness upon a gold and black tea-tray, carried it into the parlour.

10. She rapped and entered promptly. As she did so her visitor moved quickly, so that she got but a glimpse of a white object disappearing behind the table. It would seem he was picking something from the floor. She rapped the mustard pot on the table, and then she noticed the overcoat and hat had been taken off and put over a chair in front of the fire, and a pair of wet boots threatened rust to her steel fender. She went to these things resolutely. "I suppose I may have them to dry now," she said in a voice that brooked no denial.

11. "Leave the hat," said her visitor, in a muffled voice, and turning she saw he had raised his head and was sitting and looking at her.

12. For a moment she stood gaping at him, too surprised to speak.

13. He held a white cloth — it was a serviette he had brought with him — over the lower part of his face, so that his mouth and jaws were completely hidden, and that was the reason for his muffled voice. But it was not that which startled Mrs. Hall. It was the fact that all his forehead above his blue glasses was covered by a white bandage, and that another covered his ears, leaving not a scrap of his face exposed excepting only his pink, peaked nose. It was bright, pink, and shiny just as it had been at first. He wore a dark-brown velvet jacket with a high, black, linen-lined collar turned up about his neck. The thick black hair, escaping as it could below and between the cross bandages, projected in curious tails and horns, giving him the strangest appearance conceivable. This muffled and bandaged head was so unlike what she had anticipated, that for a moment she was rigid.

14. He did not remove the serviette, but remained holding it, as she saw now, with a brown gloved hand, and regarding her with his inscrutable blue glasses. "Leave the hat," he said, speaking very distinctly through the white cloth.

15. Her nerves began to recover from the shock they had received. She placed the hat on the chair again by the fire. "I didn't know, sir," she began, "that — " and she stopped embarrassed.

16. "Thank you," he said dryly, glancing from her to the door and then at her again.

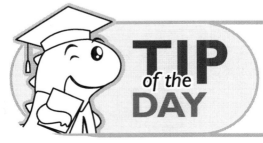

TIP of the DAY

As you are reading a fictional passage, keep track of the character motivations.
What does each character want in the story?

EXERCISES

1. Describe the visitor, in your own words. Support your analysis with at least two pieces of evidence from the text.

CCSS.ELA-LITERACY.RL.7.1

2. What does the statement below from paragraph 1 mean?

"He staggered into the Coach and Horses, more dead than alive as it seemed..."

CCSS.ELA-LITERACY.RL.7.4

3. Select the sentence from the passage that emphasizes Mrs. Hall's positive view of the visitor in the beginning.

A. "He stamped and shook the snow from off himself in the bar, and followed Mrs. Hall into her guest parlour to strike his bargain."
B. "A guest to stop in the town in the wintertime was an unheard-of piece of luck..."
C. "Although the fire was burning up briskly, she was surprised to see that her visitor still wore his hat and coat..."
D. "'Very well, sir,' she said. 'As you like. In a bit the room will be warmer.'"

CCSS.ELA-LITERACY.RL.7.1

4. Read the sentence below from the story.

She put down the eggs and bacon with considerable emphasis, and called rather than said to him, "Your lunch is served, sir."

Why did Mrs. Hall put down the food "with considerable emphasis"?

A. Mrs. Hall was clumsy and almost dropped the food.
B. The visitor had not moved, so Mrs. Hall wanted to be sure he heard her bring in the food.
C. Mrs. Hall was angry with Millie because she made mistakes.
D. Mrs. Hall was very helpful and prompt when serving meals to guests.

CCSS.ELA-LITERACY.RL.7.1

5. How does Mrs. Hall's perspective of the visitor change? Select the best answer.

A. Mrs. Hall was curious about the stranger's appearance but later was shocked.

B. Mrs. Hall found the visitor to be cheerful at first but then felt that he was rude.

C. Mrs. Hall was frightened to be near the visitor but then realized he was kind.

D. Mrs. Hall thought that he was polite at first but then felt that he was dangerous.

CCSS.ELA-LITERACY.RL.7.6

6. How does the setting help shape the story's plot?

A. The warm fire in the guest parlour intensifies the conflict.

B. The bustling kitchen supports the quick pace of the story.

C. The guest inn provides contrast for the climax of the plot.

D. The cold, snowy setting enhances the mystery about the visitor.

CCSS.ELA-LITERACY.RL.7.3

NOTES

WEEK 8

ARGOPREP.COM

VIDEO
EXPLANATIONS

economy (noun)

7th Grade Spelling Practice

CCSS.ELA-LITERACY.L.7.2.B

Word List and Definitions

You will continue to see academic words as you read textbooks and passages in all of your classes, including social studies, science, and history.

Let's review social studies words that are sometimes misspelled by students.

agriculture (noun): production of crops and livestock

boundary (noun): something that marks a limit or edge

cultural (adjective): relating to the customs, art, language of a group of people

desert (noun): an area with little to no rainfall and grows very few plants

economy (noun): a system of money, income, wealth

famine (noun): extreme lack of food across a large area of land

geography (noun): the study of climate and the earth's surface

government (noun): a group of people in a community, state, or country that is in power

political (adjective): relating to the study of government

population (noun): a group of people who live in an area; the number of people who live in an area

technology (noun): an invention, method, industrial process

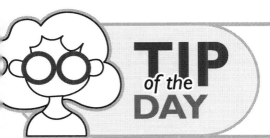

TIP *of the* DAY

Practice spelling words by repeatedly handwriting them in a notebook.

EXERCISES

Rewrite each sentence to fix any errors in spelling.

1. Early populashuns settled in an area because of agraculture.

CCSS.ELA-LITERACY.L.7.2.B

4. Medieval China had a structured goverment and advanced politacal system.

CCSS.ELA-LITERACY.L.7.2.B

2. What happens to an iconmy during a famin?

CCSS.ELA-LITERACY.L.7.2.B

5. Part of Africa is covered by the Sahara Dessert, and its boundry can be seen on a map.

CCSS.ELA-LITERACY.L.7.2.B

3. Windmills and watermills are examples of tecnoligy created during the Middle Ages.

CCSS.ELA-LITERACY.L.7.2.B

6. We are studying the cultral contributions of Medieval Japan.

CCSS.ELA-LITERACY.L.7.2.B

7th Grade Spelling Practice

CCSS.ELA-LITERACY.L.7.2.B

Word List and Definitions

Let's review academic words for science that are sometimes misspelled by students.

atmosphere (noun): the gases surrounding the earth

characteristic (noun): a quality or trait

chemical (noun): a substance produced by a chemical process

environment (noun): the living things, air, water, and minerals surrounding an area

evidence (noun): proof or facts

experiment (noun): a test that is planned to find an answer to an unknown idea

hypothesis (noun): an educated guess or prediction

inquiry (noun): a search for facts or true information

observe (verb): watch closely

pollution (noun): waste, poison, harmful substances

TIP
of the
DAY

Words can sometimes be changed from nouns to adjectives. When you read, try to spot these spelling words when they are written as other parts of speech.

EXERCISES

Rewrite each sentence to fix any errors in spelling.

1. To prove our hipothisis, we are going to abserve what happens during the experumant.

CCSS.ELA-LITERACY.L.7.2.B

2. Polution is harming the environmint.

CCSS.ELA-LITERACY.L.7.2.B

3. We began an inquirie to find out if music helps plants grow.

CCSS.ELA-LITERACY.L.7.2.B

4. The evidance showed us that a cemical reaction had taken place.

CCSS.ELA-LITERACY.L.7.2.B

5. The atmosfear is mostly made up of nitrogen.

CCSS.ELA-LITERACY.L.7.2.B

6. A caracteristic of a frog is its smooth, slimy skin.

CCSS.ELA-LITERACY.L.7.2.B

7th Grade Spelling Practice

CCSS.ELA-LITERACY.L.7.2.B

Word List and Definitions

Let's review academic words for math that are sometimes misspelled by students.

calculate (verb): compute or determine a mathematical answer

decimal (noun): a number in the base ten system

estimate (verb): a careful guess

equivalent (adjective or noun): same or equal

minimum (noun): least possible amount or smallest number

maximum (noun): greatest possible amount or largest number

perimeter (noun): the length of all sides

probability (noun): the number that shows how likely something is to happen

symmetry (noun): when both sides of something are the same or similar in form

variable (noun): a symbol for the number that is not yet known

TIP of the DAY

Practice spelling by spelling your words out loud. If you are an auditory learner, this can be especially helpful!

EXERCISES

Rewrite each sentence to fix any errors in spelling.

1. We calcilated the peremeter of the rectangle.

CCSS.ELA-LITERACY.L.7.2.B

2. Figure out the varable in the equation.

CCSS.ELA-LITERACY.L.7.2.B

3. When you split a circle in half, each side has symitry.

CCSS.ELA-LITERACY.L.7.2.B

4. Show the minamum and maxamum on the number line.

CCSS.ELA-LITERACY.L.7.2.B

5. Estumate the probabilty that Jennifer will choose a green card.

CCSS.ELA-LITERACY.L.7.2.B

6. Round the number to the nearest decimil.

CCSS.ELA-LITERACY.L.7.2.B

: **VIDEO**
EXPLANATIONS ▶

ARGOPREP.COM

A Christmas Carol *by Charles Dickens*

The passage below from the novella A Christmas Carol *follows the main character Ebenezer Scrooge.*

1. Oh! But he was a tight-fisted hand at the grindstone, Scrooge: a squeezing, wrenching, grasping, scraping, clutching, covetous old sinner! Hard and sharp as flint, from which no steel had ever struck out generous fire; secret, and self-contained, and solitary as an oyster. The cold within him froze his old features, nipped his pointed nose, shrivelled his cheek, stiffened his gait; made his eyes red, his thin lips blue; and spoke out shrewdly in his grating voice. A frosty rime was on his head, and on his eyebrows, and his wiry chin. He carried his own low temperature always about with him; he iced his office in the dog-days; and didn't thaw it one degree at Christmas.

2. External heat and cold had little influence on Scrooge. No warmth could warm, nor wintry weather chill him. No wind that blew was bitterer than he, no falling snow was more intent upon its purpose, no pelting rain less open to entreaty. Foul weather didn't know where to have him. The heaviest rain, and snow, and hail, and sleet, could boast of the advantage over him in only one respect. They often "came down" handsomely, and Scrooge never did.

3. Nobody ever stopped him in the street to say, with gladsome looks, "My dear Scrooge, how are you? when will you come to see me?" No beggars implored him to bestow a trifle, no children asked him what it was o'clock, no man or woman ever once in all his life inquired the way to such and such a place, of Scrooge. Even the blindmen's dogs appeared to know him; and when they saw him coming on, would tug their owners into doorways and up courts; and then would wag their tails as though they said, "no eye at all is better than an evil eye, dark master!"

4. But what did Scrooge care? It was the very thing he liked. To edge his way along the crowded paths of life, warning all human sympathy to keep its distance, was what the knowing ones call "nuts" to Scrooge.

5. Once upon a time — of all the good days in the year, on Christmas Eve — old Scrooge sat busy in his counting-house. It was cold, bleak, biting weather; foggy; and he could hear the people in the court outside go wheezing up and down, beating their hands upon their breasts, and stamping their feet upon the pavement-stones to warm them. The city clocks had only just gone three in the afternoon, but it was quite dark already: it had not been light all day: and candles were flaring in the windows of the neighbouring offices, like ruddy smears upon the palpable brown air. The fog came pouring in at every chink and keyhole, and was so dense without, that although the court was of the narrowest, the houses opposite were mere phantoms. To see the dingy cloud come drooping down, obscuring everything, one might have thought that Nature lived hard by, and was brewing on a large scale.

6. The door of Scrooge's counting-house was open that he might keep his eye upon his clerk, who in a dismal little cell beyond, a sort of tank, was copying letters. Scrooge had a very small fire, but the clerk's fire was so very much smaller that it looked like one coal. But he couldn't replenish it, for Scrooge kept the coal-box in his own room; and so surely as the clerk came in with the shovel, the master predicted that it would be necessary for them to part. Wherefore the clerk put on his white comforter, and tried to warm himself at the candle; in which effort, not being a man of a strong imagination, he failed.

7. "A merry Christmas, uncle! God save you!" cried a cheerful voice. It was the voice of Scrooge's nephew, who came upon him so quickly that this was the first intimation he had of his approach.

8. "Bah!" said Scrooge, "Humbug!"

9. He had so heated himself with rapid walking in the fog and frost, this nephew of Scrooge's, that he was all in a glow; his face was ruddy and handsome; his eyes sparkled, and his breath smoked again.

10. "Christmas a humbug, uncle!" said Scrooge's nephew. "You don't mean that, I am sure."

11. "I do," said Scrooge. "Merry Christmas! what right have you to be merry? what reason have you to be merry? You're poor enough."

12. "Come, then," returned the nephew gaily. "What right have you to be dismal? what reason have you to be morose? You're rich enough."

13. Scrooge having no better answer ready on the spur of the moment, said, "Bah!" again; and followed it up with "Humbug."

14. "Don't be cross, uncle," said the nephew.

15. "What else can I be" returned the uncle, "when I live in such a world of fools as this? Merry Christmas! Out upon merry Christmas! What's Christmas time to you but a time for paying bills without money; a time for finding yourself a year older, and not an hour richer; a time for balancing your books and having every item in 'em through a round dozen of months presented dead against you? If I could work my will," said Scrooge, indignantly, "every idiot who goes about with 'Merry Christmas' on his lips, should be boiled with his own pudding, and buried with a stake of holly through his heart. He should!"

16. "Uncle!" pleaded the nephew.

17. "Nephew!" returned the uncle, sternly, "keep Christmas in your own way, and let me keep it in mine."

18. "Keep it!" repeated Scrooge's nephew. "But you don't keep it."

19. "Let me leave it alone, then," said Scrooge. "Much good may it do you! Much good it has ever done you!"

20. "There are many things from which I might have derived good, by which I have not profited, I dare say," returned the nephew: "Christmas among the rest. But I am sure I have always thought of Christmas time, when it has come round—apart from the veneration due to its sacred name and origin, if anything belonging to it can be apart from that—as a good time: a kind, forgiving, charitable, pleasant time: the only time I know of, in the long calendar of the year, when men and women seem by one consent to open their shut-up hearts freely, and to think of people below them as if they really were fellow-passengers to the grave, and not another race of creatures bound on other journeys. And therefore, uncle, though it has never put a scrap of gold or silver in my pocket, I believe that it has done me good, and will do me good; and I say, God bless it!"

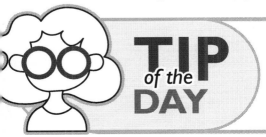

TIP
of the
DAY

Sometimes the main character of a story is an antihero. An antihero is a main character who does not have the traits of a hero. An antihero may not be as kind or as courageous as a typical hero in a story. Would you consider Scrooge an antihero or a hero in this passage?

1. What does the following figurative language from paragraph 1 mean?

   "The cold within him froze his old features..."

   A. It is winter and cold outside.
   B. Scrooge wants to find a place that is warm.
   C. Scrooge is mean and unfriendly.
   D. Scrooge is feeling sick.

   CCSS.ELA-LITERACY.RL.7.4

3. What does the word "obscuring" mean as it is used in paragraph 5? Select the best answer.

   A. covering
   B. polluting
   C. brightening
   D. showing

   CCSS.ELA-LITERACY.RL.7.4

2. How do paragraphs 2 and 3 impact the story? Select the best answer.

   A. They foreshadow the resolution between Scrooge and the town's citizens.
   B. They describe the wintry setting.
   C. They emphasize a major plot point between Scrooge and the blindmen's dogs.
   D. They provide supporting evidence that Scrooge is an unpleasant man.

   CCSS.ELA-LITERACY.RL.7.3

4. What is the purpose of paragraph 9 in the story?

   A. It describes how the setting has changed to a warm environment.
   B. It emphasizes that Scrooge's nephew is his opposite.
   C. It creates a solution to Scrooge's problem of not liking Christmas.
   D. It proves that Scrooge and his family members are similar.

   CCSS.ELA-LITERACY.RL.7.3

5. Why does Scrooge say that his nephew has no right to be "merry"? Select the best answer.

    A. Scrooges says that it is too cold outside to feel happy.
    B. Scrooge says that his nephew is poor.
    C. Scrooge says that Christmas is too focused on buying gifts.
    D. Scrooge says that his nephew rarely visits him.

    CCSS.ELA-LITERACY.RL.7.1

6. Which detail from the story best highlights how the nephew's view of Christmas contrasts with Scrooge's viewpoint? Select the best answer.

    A. "What's Christmas time to you but a time for paying bills without money..."
    B. "But you don't keep it."
    C. "But I am sure I have always thought of Christmas time, when it has come round..."
    D. "...a good time: a kind, forgiving, charitable, pleasant time..."

    CCSS.ELA-LITERACY.RL.7.6

NOTES

WEEK 9 : WEDNESDAY

Jabberwocky *by Lewis Carroll*

This poem first appeared in Lewis Carroll's novel Through the Looking-Glass, *which was a sequel to* Alice's Adventures in Wonderland.

'Twas brillig, and the slithy toves
Did gyre and gimble in the wabe:
All mimsy were the borogoves,
And the mome raths outgrabe.

'Beware the Jabberwock, my son!
The jaws that bite, the claws that catch!
Beware the Jubjub bird, and shun
The frumious Bandersnatch!'

He took his vorpal sword in hand:
Long time the manxome foe he sought —
So rested he by the Tumtum tree,

And stood a while in thought.

And, as in uffish thought he stood,
The Jabberwock, with eyes of flame,
Came whiffling through the tulgey wood,
And burbled as it came!

One two! One two! And through and through
The vorpal blade went snicker-snack!
He left it dead, and with its head
He went galumphing back.

'And hast thou slain the Jabberwock?
Come to my arms, my beamish boy!
Oh frabjous day! Callooh! Callay!'
He chortled in his joy.

'Twas brillig, and the slithy toves
Did gyre and gimble in the wabe:
All mimsy were the borogoves,
And the mome raths outgrabe.

This poem is called a «nonsense poem» because it uses imaginary words created by Carroll.

EXERCISES

1. Carroll created new words in this poem. What kind of tone does he establish with the new words?

    A. a serious tone
    B. a calm tone
    C. a playful tone
    D. a horrifying tone

    CCSS.ELA-LITERACY.RL.7.4

2. What is the central idea of stanza 2?

    A. The stanza characterizes poisonous plants.
    B. The stanza characterizes dangerous people.
    C. The stanza characterizes friendly animals.
    D. The stanza characterizes threatening beasts.

    CCSS.ELA-LITERACY.RL.7.2

3. The author separates the line, "And stood a while in thought" from the other stanzas. What effect does this have on the poem's meaning?

    A. It explains that the hero was tired from his journey to find the Jabberwocky.
    B. It explains that the hero was frightened and alone.
    C. It explains that the hero did not expect the Jabberwocky to attack.
    D. It explains that the hero was thinking about his home and family.

    CCSS.ELA-LITERACY.RL.7.5

4. What common theme is found in the poem? Select the best answer.

    A. change versus tradition
    B. good versus evil
    C. fear of failure
    D. power and corruption

    CCSS.ELA-LITERACY.RL.7.2

5. How does the rhyme scheme in stanza 1 contrast with the rhyme scheme in stanza 2?

    A. Stanza 1's rhyme scheme is abab, while stanza 2's rhyme scheme is cdcd.
    B. Stanza 1's rhyme scheme is aabb, while stanza 2's rhyme scheme is cddd.
    C. Stanza 1's rhyme scheme is aaab, while stanza 2's rhyme scheme is ccdd.
    D. Stanza 1's rhyme scheme is abbb, while stanza 2's rhyme scheme is cccd.

    CCSS.ELA-LITERACY.RL.7.4

6. Why are the lines of the first stanza repeated in the final stanza? Select the best answer.

    A. It indicates that the hero has returned home.
    B. It enhances the theme of the poem.
    C. It clarifies how long the hero's journey was.
    D. It illustrates the dangers of the Jabberwocky.

    CCSS.ELA-LITERACY.RL.7.5

WEEK 9 : FRIDAY

Adapted from Chapultepec Castle
by Lorena Gathereau

Introduction

1. Chapultepec (chə-pūl'tə-pĕk') Castle (or Castillo de Chapultepec) sits atop Chapultepec Hill in Mexico City. The word Chapultepec is a Nahuatl (language of the Aztecs) word meaning "grasshopper's hill." The name refers to the hill's shape, which resembles a grasshopper. The area surrounding the castle is known as the Bosque de Chapultepec (literally "Chapultepec Forest," but better known as "Chapultepec Park" in English). It is Latin America's largest urban park.

Pre-Hispanic Importance

2. Chapultepec Hill shows anthropological evidence of the presence of different groups of people, including the Toltec and the Aztecs. After the Aztecs founded the city of Tenochtitlan (modern-day Mexico City) in 1325, Chapultepec Hill was considered to be a sacred place. Throughout the following years, Aztec rulers ordered several changes to the hill and forest.

3. In 1428, the Aztec king of Texcoco, Netzahualcóyotl, built a retreat and improved the forest's flora and fauna. Then in 1465, Moctezuma Ilhuicamina ordered that his image be carved in rock at the bottom of the hill and the construction of the Tlaxpana aqueduct. In 1507, Moctezuma Xocoyotzin had pools created to raise exotic fish and serve as water storage; he ordered that plants and trees from across the empire be planted in the Chapultepec forest. In 1521, Cuauhtémoc defended Chapultepec against the Spaniards. Hernán Cortés then took possession of Chapultepec, giving Captain Julián Jaramillo the northern section. In 1530, a royal decree ruled that the Bosque de Chapultepec belonged to Mexico City.

Spanish Colonial Period

4. During the Spanish Colonial period, Chapultepec Hill was still considered to be one of the area's most beautiful places, suitable for retreats. In 1785, under the rule of New Spain's Viceroy Bernardo de Gálvez, construction began on a country house at the top of Chapultepec Hill. The architect in charge was Lieutenant Colonel of the Spanish Army and engineer Francisco Bambitelli. When Bambitelli had to depart to Havana, Cuba, the Captain of the infantry and engineer Manuel Agustín Mascaró took over the project. Despite rapid progress on the project, Viceroy Bernardo de Gálvez died in 1786 before its completion; it was speculated that he was poisoned for actually designing a fortress, rather than a country house, from where he could lead a revolt against the Spanish Crown.

5. As a result, the Crown ordered a halt to the construction and attempted to auction it off at the price of 60 thousand pesos (even though they had already spent over 300 thousand pesos on its construction up to that point). Due to a lack of interest in the building, Viceroy Juan Vicente de Güemes Pacheco y Padilla, the 2nd Count of Revillagigedo, ordered that the building be used to house the Kingdom of New Spain's General Archive. This project also failed.

6. In 1806, Mexico City's municipal government finally purchased the building and surrounding forest. The building remained abandoned, however, during Mexico's War of Independence. In 1833, it became the Military Academy.

7. Due to the strategic location and fortress-like surroundings of the building, Chapultepec Castle served as a military post during the Mexican American War (1846-1848) and stood as Mexico City's last line of defense against the US American army. The Battle of Chapultepec (Sept. 12-13, 1847) was the last battle before the US captured Mexico City, ending the war.

Los Niños Héroes (The Boy Heroes)

8. Mexican legend holds that during the Battle of Chapultepec, six brave teenage cadets refused to abandon their posts and died defending their country. Their names were: Juan de la Barrera, Juan Escutia, Francisco Marquez, Agustin Melgar, Fernando Montes de Oca, and Vicente Suarez. The final survivor, Juan Escutia, is said to have wrapped himself in the Mexican flag and jumped from the castle roof to prevent the flag from falling into enemy hands.

Royal and Presidential Palace

9. In 1864, during the Franco Mexican War (also known as the French Intervention), the French-imposed sovereigns, Emperor Maximiliano and Empress Carlota, chose to live in the castle. They hired several Austrian, French, Belgian, and Mexican architects to improve the castle's living conditions. In order to connect Chapultepec to Mexico City, Emperor Maximilian commissioned the creation of a boulevard called Paseo de la Emperatriz (the Empress' Promenade). Today, this boulevard is named Paseo de la Reforma (Reform Promenade). Maximiliano and Carlota also had vast improvements made to the castle's rooftop garden.

10. After the fall of the Second Empire of Mexico in 1867, the castle remained abandoned for almost ten years. In 1876, it was designated as the Astronomical, Meteorological, and Magnetic Observatory ("Antecedentes Históricas"). The Observatory, however, was moved to a different site in 1883 and the Military College once again had access to the grounds. The castle then underwent renovations in order to serve as a presidential palace for years to come ("Antecedentes Históricas").

Chapultepec Castle Today

11. Chapultepec Castle's last designation occurred in February 1939, when President Lázaro Cárdenas ordered the creation of the National Institute for Anthropology and History, naming the castle as the location of the Museo Nacional de Historia. Today, a part of the castle houses various museum collections and shows off the elegant European decor and furniture of the castle's heyday.

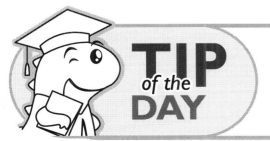

TIP of the DAY

Writers use transitional words and phrase to transition smoothly between ideas. Can you spot the transitions used in this passage?

EXERCISES

1. Describe two ways that Aztec rulers made changes to Chapultepec Hill. Include two pieces of evidence from the text to support your response.

_____

_____

CCSS.ELA-LITERACY.RI.7.1

2. Why did the Spanish crown stop the construction of the country house at the top of Chapultepec Hill?

_____

_____

CCSS.ELA-LITERACY.RI.7.3

3. Why does the author include parentheses throughout the passage?

   A. The author includes statements from scholars inside the parentheses.
   B. The author strengthens arguments by including parentheses.
   C. The author adds additional clarifying information inside parentheses.
   D. The author adds contrasting information inside the parentheses.

CCSS.ELA-LITERACY.RI.7.5

4. Which text structure does the author primarily use in the passage?

   A. cause and effect
   B. problem and solution
   C. sequential order
   D. chronological order

CCSS.ELA-LITERACY.RI.7.5

5. How is Chapultepec Castle used today?

   A. It is used as a military post.
   B. It is used as a hotel.
   C. It is used as an astronomical observatory.
   D. It is used as a museum.

CCSS.ELA-LITERACY.RI.7.1

6. How does paragraph 4 relate to paragraph 7?

   A. Paragraph 4 states who managed the construction of the country house, and paragraph 7 explains that they caused the Mexican American War.
   B. Paragraph 4 explains that the country house was built as a fortress, and paragraph 7 explains that those traits later turned it into a military post.
   C. Paragraph 4 describes a key military figure, and paragraph 7 describes The Battle of Chapultepec.
   D. Paragraph 4 highlights the Spanish Colonial era, and paragraph 7 explains how it ended.

CCSS.ELA-LITERACY.RI.7.5

WEEK 10

: VIDEO ▶ EXPLANATIONS

ARGOPREP.COM

Eduardo sprinted across the field.

Using Precise Language

CCSS.ELA-LITERACY.L.7.3.A

<u>Key Terms and Examples</u>

What is precise language?

We use precise language to strengthen our writing and be clear, rather than vague, about ideas. While there are a variety of ways to include precise language in our writing, here are three easy ways to start.

Precise Verbs

Use verbs that are specific and refreshing instead of using common verbs.

<u>Examples</u>

Eduardo <u>ran</u> across the soccer field.
Precise verb included: Eduardo <u>sprinted</u> across the field.

Vanessa drank a glass of water.
Precise verb included: Vanessa <u>guzzled</u> a glass of water.

Precise Adjectives

Use creative adjectives to create more engaging and precise sentences.

<u>Examples</u>

Jess looked <u>pretty</u> in the new dress.
Precise adjective included: Jess looked <u>exquisite</u> in the new dress.

The weather was <u>hot</u>.
Precise adjective included: The weather was sweltering.

Precise Adverbs

Add adverbs to sentences in order to express an idea more precisely, or change existing adverbs so that they are precise.

<u>Examples</u>

The cat jumped onto the table.
Precise adverb included: The cat jumped <u>gracefully</u> onto the table.

The fire alarm rang <u>loudly</u> throughout the building.
Precise adverb included: The fire alarm rang <u>deafeningly</u> throughout the building.

TIP of the DAY

A thesaurus can help you find synonyms so that you can include precise verbs, adjectives, and adverbs in your writing.

EXERCISES

Read each sentence. Then select the answer that best represents a precise language replacement for the underlined word.

Rewrite each sentence to include precise language.

---

1. The deer ran <u>quickly</u>.

   A. fast
   B. swiftly
   C. nicely
   D. no change

   CCSS.ELA-LITERACY.L.7.3.A

4. Jasmine threw the ball.

   _____

   _____

   _____

   CCSS.ELA-LITERACY.L.7.3.A

---

2. The rotten food smelled <u>bad</u>.

   A. off
   B. poor
   C. revolting
   D. no change

   CCSS.ELA-LITERACY.L.7.3.A

5. The soup tasted good.

   _____

   _____

   _____

   CCSS.ELA-LITERACY.L.7.3.A

---

3. Tomiko <u>jumped</u> over the hole.

   A. stepped
   B. walked
   C. vaulted
   D. no change

   CCSS.ELA-LITERACY.L.7.3.A

6. The caterpillar moved slowly across the leaf.

   _____

   _____

   _____

   CCSS.ELA-LITERACY.L.7.3.A

Expressing Ideas Concisely

CCSS.ELA-LITERACY.L.7.3.A

Key Terms

What is concise language?

When you use concise language, you communicate your point quickly to keep the reader's attention. Your writing should express exactly what you mean without adding unnecessary words.

Examples

Negative Phrases

Negative phrases often use extra words. When we take out words such as "not," "no," or "nothing," the sentence will become more concise.

The sink was <u>not working properly</u>.

Concise version: The sink was broken.

Unnecessary Modifiers

Unnecessary modifiers can include: very, really, totally, so, sort of, kind of, just, always, usually. Eliminating these modifiers will produce a concise sentence.

The school dance is going to be <u>really</u> fun, but I <u>kind of just</u> want to go with friends.

Concise version: The school dance is going to be fun, but I only want to go with friends.

Cliches

Cliches are overused phrases. Avoiding them will make your writing more concise.

When it comes to Cody and his dad, <u>the apple doesn't fall far from the tree</u>.

Concise version: Cody and his dad are alike.

TIP of the DAY

Using precise and concise language should also apply to speaking. Think about how you are communicating ideas when speaking.

EXERCISES

Rewrite each sentence so that it is concise.

1. After we apologize, my mom always tell us that actions speak louder than words.

2. The cookie jar had no cookies left in it.

3. Kim totally will win first place because she always is the best dancer.

4. Mrs. Tuttle had no patience left for the noisy class.

5. Even though the judges did not like his dish, the chef remembered that you can't please everyone.

6. The sunset looks so very gorgeous, so I really think we should stay at the beach.

Redundancy

CCSS.ELA-LITERACY.L.7.3.A

Key Terms

What does redundancy mean?

Redundancy is the unnecessary repetition of ideas. Our writing should be clear and to the point, and we should eliminate words that are too similar.

Examples

Redundant version: The carnival was <u>entertaining</u> and <u>enjoyable</u>.
Edited version: The carnival was entertaining.

Redundant version: Lucia's <u>personal opinion</u> is that dogs are amazing pets.
Edited version: Lucia's opinion is that dogs are amazing pets.

Redundant version: The ocean is <u>peaceful</u> and <u>calm</u>.
Edited version: The ocean is peaceful.

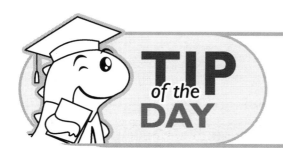

When editing writing for redundancy, check if there are two synonyms with the same meaning.

EXERCISES

Rewrite each sentence to eliminate redundancy.

1. The tall and towering man had to duck under the door.

   _____

   _____

   _____

   CCSS.ELA-LITERACY.L.7.3.A

2. We joined together in a circle.

   _____

   _____

   _____

   CCSS.ELA-LITERACY.L.7.3.A

3. The three girls form a trio singing group.

   _____

   _____

   _____

   CCSS.ELA-LITERACY.L.7.3.A

Read each sentence. Select the word that is redundant.

4. The restaurant gave Dan a free complimentary slice of cake.

   A. restaurant
   B. gave
   C. complimentary
   D. slice

   CCSS.ELA-LITERACY.L.7.3.A

5. In today's modern society, we can find out anything on our phones.

   A. modern
   B. society
   C. find
   D. anything

   CCSS.ELA-LITERACY.L.7.3.A

6. The last and final movie scene was shocking.

   A. the
   B. last
   C. scene
   D. shocking

   CCSS.ELA-LITERACY.L.7.3.A

WEEK 11

WEEK 11 : MONDAY

Adapted from The Count of Monte Cristo *by Alexandre Dumas*

In this excerpt of the novel, a large boat, the Pharaon, arrives in the harbor of Marseille, France. The Pharaon has three masts (the poles that rise from the ship and hold the sails). A crowd forms to watch the boat arrive.

1. On February 24, 1815, the look-out in Marseille signaled the arrival of the Pharaon, a three-masted ship that had traveled from Smyrna, Trieste, and Naples.

2. Immediately, and according to custom, the incoming ship drew spectators; it is always a big event at Marseilles for a ship to come into port, especially when this ship, like the Pharaon, had been built, rigged, and laden in the city, and belonged to a local ship owner.

3. The ship sailed on and approached the harbor under topsails, jib, and spanker, but moved so slowly and sedately that the people in the crowd asked one another what misfortune could have happened on board. However, those experienced in navigation saw plainly that if any accident had occurred, it had been not to the vessel itself because it was under control. The pilot, who was steering the Pharaon towards the narrow entrance of the inner port, was a young man, who, with activity and vigilant eye, watched every motion of the ship, and repeated each direction of the pilot.

4. The unease among the spectators had so much affected one man that he jumped into a small boat and asked the rower to take him to the Pharaon. They pulled up alongside the ship as it rounded into La Réserve basin.

5. When the young man on board saw this person approach, he left his station by the pilot, and, hat in hand, leaned over the ship's bulwarks.

6. He was a fine, tall, slim young fellow of eighteen or twenty, with black eyes, and hair as dark as a raven's wing. He had the calmness and resolution of someone who had faced danger since childhood.

7. "Ah, is it you, Dantès?" cried the man in the skiff. "What's the matter? And why have you such an air of sadness aboard?"

8. "A great misfortune, Monsieur Morrel," replied the young man, "a great misfortune, for me especially! Off Civita Vecchia we lost our brave Captain Leclere."

9. "And the cargo?" inquired the owner, eagerly.

10. "Is all safe, Monsieur Morrel; and I think you will be satisfied on that head. But poor Captain Leclere —"

11. "What happened to him?" asked the owner, with an air of considerable relief. "What happened to the worthy captain?"

12. "He died."

13. "Fell into the sea?"

14. "No, sir, he died of brain-fever in dreadful agony." Then turning to the crew, he said, "Bear a hand there, to take in sail!"

15. All hands obeyed, and at once the eight or ten seamen who composed the crew, sprang to their respective stations at the spanker brails and outhaul, topsail sheets and halyards, the jib downhaul, and the topsail clewlines and buntlines. The young sailor gave a look to see that his orders were promptly and accurately obeyed, and then turned again to the owner.

16. "And how did this misfortune occur?" inquired the man, resuming the interrupted conversation.

17. "Alas, sir, in the most unexpected manner. After a long talk with the harbor-master, Captain Leclere left Naples greatly disturbed in mind. In twenty-four hours he was attacked by a fever, and died three days afterwards. We performed the usual burial service, and he is at his rest, sewn up in his hammock off El Giglio island. We bring his widow his sword and cross of honor. It was worthwhile, truly," added the young man with a melancholy smile, "to make war against the English for ten years, and to die in his bed at last, like everybody else."

18. "Why, you see, Edmond," replied the owner, who appeared more comforted at every moment, "we are all mortal, and the old must make way for the young. If not, why, there would be no promotion; and since you assure me that the cargo —"

19. "Is all safe and sound, Monsieur Morrel, take my word for it; and I advise you not to take 25,000 francs for the profits of the voyage."

20. Then, as they were just passing the Round Tower, the young man shouted: "Stand by there to lower the topsails and jib; brail up the spanker!"

21. The order was executed promptly.

22. "Let go — and clue up!" At this last command all the sails were lowered, and the vessel moved almost imperceptibly onwards.

23. "Now, if you will come on board, Monsieur Morrel," said Dantès, observing the owner's impatience, "here is Monsieur Danglars, coming out of his cabin, who will give you all the details. As for me, I must look after the anchoring."

TIP of the DAY

To help you understand a fictional story, think about each event that happens in the story, or the plot.

EXERCISES

1. According to the passage, what is one reason the Pharaon's arrival drew a crowd?

   A. The ship's arrival was later than expected.
   B. Marseille does not normally see ships.
   C. The ship's pilot was a stranger.
   D. The ship was built in Marseille.

   CCSS.ELA-LITERACY.RL.7.1

2. Why did the man asked to be rowed out to the ship?

   A. He saw that Captain Leclere was not leading the ship.
   B. He was excited to greet the members of the ship.
   C. He was concerned because the ship was moving slowly.
   D. He needed to pay the ship's crew members.

   CCSS.ELA-LITERACY.RL.7.1

3. What type of figurative language can be found in the following sentence from paragraph 6?

   He was a fine, tall, slim young fellow of eighteen or twenty, with black eyes, and hair as dark as a raven's wing.

   A. hyperbole
   B. personification
   C. metaphor
   D. simile

   CCSS.ELA-LITERACY.RL.7.4

4. Select the detail from the passage that best explains why the young man is leading the ship.

   A. "The pilot, who was steering the Pharaon towards the narrow entrance of the inner port, was a young man..."
   B. "When the young man on board saw this person approach, he left his station by the pilot..."
   C. "Off Civita Vecchia we lost our brave Captain Leclere."
   D. "As for me, I must look after the anchoring."

   CCSS.ELA-LITERACY.RL.7.1

EXERCISES

5. How does Monsieur Morrel's point of view contrast with the young man's perspective?

   A. Monsieur Morrel is more concerned about the cargo than Captain Leclere.
   B. Monsieur Morrel is more concerned about Captain Leclere than the cargo.
   C. Monsieur Morrel is more concerned about the young man's ability to lead.
   D. Monsieur Morrel is more concerned about the health of the men on board.

   CCSS.ELA-LITERACY.RL.7.6

6. What does the word "melancholy" mean as it is used in paragraph 17? Select the best answer.

   A. cheerful
   B. sad
   C. bored
   D. angry

   CCSS.ELA-LITERACY.RL.7.4

NOTES

Adapted from Ray Brown *by Catherine-Schmidt Jones*

Background and Influence

1. Ray Brown is considered to be one of the top bassists in jazz during the bebop era. Brown's solo work is considered to be inventive and ambitious, while remaining singable and strongly swinging. He composed, and he led recording sessions featuring outstanding jazz musicians. He was also important as a teacher and promoter in many jazz musicians' careers.

2. While Brown is respected for his solo work, those who worked with him agreed that his true genius lay in his ability to function as bass player in a music ensemble. His tone quality and accuracy of pitch are legendary among bass players, many of whom claim to be able to recognize his sound from only a few notes on any recording. Bassist Hal Gaynor, said, "He had this clarity of sound, and his intonation! At that time most bass players were playing kind of thumpy. You didn't have to recognize all the notes so long as you felt the pulse."

3. Jay Leonhart agreed, "such a huge sound and such accuracy... nobody's ever played like that since. And many of us have tried." It required unusual physical strength in the hands in order to get a sound that was both quite loud and that lasted an unusually long time for a plucked string bass note.

4. As Bill Crow explained, "He developed a lot of the skills that became the standards of the next generation of virtuoso bassists. Ray developed his technique before the invention of amplifiers and metal strings. He knew how to project his tone, and he pulled the strings percussively, making the bass line powerfully propel the rhythm section and the band."

5. Brown attributed his sound to his instrument, which was unusually thick and had a very woody tone, but many musicians have attested to the fact that he could pick up any instrument and make it "sound like Ray." Oscar Peterson said simply, "He is a walking sound. Ray has a sound that he walks around with that he can't even describe, within himself."

How He Became a Musician

6. Raymond Matthews Brown was born in Pittsburgh, Pennsylvania, on October 13, 1926. His first instrument was piano. His father wanted him to learn to play like Fats Waller, and by age eight he was memorizing Waller recordings. Ray later gave up the piano, though. He said, "I couldn't find my way on it. It just didn't give me what I wanted. Besides, I was in a high school orchestra and there must have been fourteen piano players in it."

7. The school owned a bass that he could use, so he began playing bass. He was allowed to bring it home on weekends so that he could practice. However, after Brown's picture was published in the local newspaper in reference to a paid gig that he was playing — with the school bass — he was no longer allowed to take it home, and his father finally bought him one.

8. Brown was already getting offers to join professional jazz bands on road trips, but his mother felt very strongly that he should finish high school. He left town immediately after graduation in 1944 to spend eight months with Jimmy Hinsley's band, then another eight months with Luis (Snookum) Russell's band. In 1945, while Russell's band was in Miami, Brown felt ready to try his luck in New York. The night he arrived in New York, Brown took his bags to his aunt's place and immediately asked his cousin to show him where 52nd Street, the center of jazz, was.

9. Ray recalled, "That night, I saw Erroll Garner, Art Tatum, Billie Holiday, Billie Daniels, Coleman Hawkins, and Hank Jones. I'd known Hank before. While we were talking, he said, 'Dizzy Gillespie just came in.'

10. I said, 'Where? Introduce me! I want to meet him.'" Dizzy Gillespie was another famous jazz musician; he specialized in the trumpet.

11. "So Hank introduced us. Hank said to Dizzy, 'This is Ray Brown, a friend of mine, and a very good bass player.'

12. "Dizzy said, 'You want a gig?' I almost had a heart attack! Dizzy said, 'Be at my house for rehearsal at 7 o'clock tomorrow.'

13. "I went up there the next night and got the fright of my life. The band consisted of Dizzy, Bud Powell, Max Roach, Charlie Parker — and me!'" Brown was only eighteen years old.

TIP of the DAY

Authors of informational texts often include quotes from interviews with people. People with first-hand knowledge of the person or topic are appropriate to interview because they can provide facts.

EXERCISES

1. Which statement reveals a central idea of the passage?

   A. "He was also important as a teacher and promoter in many jazz musicians' careers."
   B. "While Brown is respected for his solo work, those who worked with him agreed that his true genius lay in his ability to function as bass player in a music ensemble."
   C. "At that time most bass players were playing kind of thumpy."
   D. "His father wanted him to learn to play like Fats Waller, and by age eight he was memorizing Waller recordings."

   CCSS.ELA-LITERACY.RI.7.2

2. What was unique about Brown's ability to play the bass? Select the best answer.

   A. He was respected for his solo work.
   B. He had a sound like no other musician.
   C. He used an amplifier to create his sound.
   D. He played in his high school orchestra.

   CCSS.ELA-LITERACY.RI.7.1

3. What is the author's purpose for including paragraph 5? Select the best answer.

   A. The author wanted to quote a famous musician.
   B. The author wanted to provide a transitional paragraph.
   C. The author wanted to emphasize Brown's talent.
   D. The author wanted to provide support for paragraph 4.

   CCSS.ELA-LITERACY.RI.7.6

4. Which two text structures does the author use in the passage?

   A. sequential order, cause and effect
   B. compare and contrast, problem and solution
   C. chronological order, cause and effect
   D. description, chronological order

   CCSS.ELA-LITERACY.RI.7.5

5. Why did Ray decide to move to New York City?

   A. He was asked to move there and join a jazz band.
   B. He wanted to meet Dizzy Gillespie.
   C. Many important jazz musicians lived in New York City.
   D. Hank Jones invited him.

CCSS.ELA-LITERACY.RI.7.3

6. Which statement could act as a concluding sentence in a summary of the passage?

   A. At the age of eighteen, Brown joined respected musicians in a band.
   B. Brown had to go to rehearsal at 7 o'clock the next day.
   C. Brown could not believe he had met Dizzy Gillespie.
   D. Brown moved in with his aunt and cousin.

CCSS.ELA-LITERACY.RI.7.2

NOTES

The Road Not Taken *by Robert Frost*

Two roads diverged in a yellow wood,
And sorry I could not travel both
And be one traveler, long I stood
And looked down one as far as I could
To where it bent in the undergrowth;

Then took the other, as just as fair,
And having perhaps the better claim,
Because it was grassy and wanted wear;
Though as for that the passing there
Had worn them really about the same,

And both that morning equally lay
In leaves no step had trodden black.
Oh, I kept the first for another day!
Yet knowing how way leads on to way,
I doubted if I should ever come back.

I shall be telling this with a sigh
Somewhere ages and ages hence:
Two roads diverged in a wood, and I —
I took the one less traveled by,
And that has made all the difference.

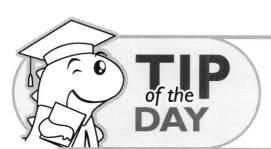

TIP of the DAY

Robert Frost wrote many poems about nature. When you read his poems, think about how nature relates to his message.

EXERCISES

1. What does the word "diverged" mean in the first stanza? Explain how you determined the meaning.

_____

_____

_____

_____

_____

CCSS.ELA-LITERACY.RL.7.4

2. Describe the poem's setting. Use two details from the text in your response.

_____

_____

_____

_____

_____

CCSS.ELA-LITERACY.RL.7.2

3. What does "trodden" mean in stanza 3? Select the best answer.

A. walked
B. painted
C. swept
D. fallen

CCSS.ELA-LITERACY.RL.7.4

4. How do the following lines from stanza 3 impact the meaning of the poem?

*Yet knowing how way leads on to way, /
I doubted if I should ever come back.*

A. The narrator is confused about the path.
B. The narrator regrets what has happened.
C. The narrator has come to his favorite place.
D. The narrator has made a decision.

CCSS.ELA-LITERACY.RL.7.4

5. Why did the author conclude the poem with the following lines?

I took the one less traveled by, / And that has made all the difference.

A. The lines contrast with the theme of the poem.
B. The lines reflect the main idea of the first stanza.
C. The lines communicate the narrator's conflict.
D. The lines emphasize the title of the poem.

CCSS.ELA-LITERACY.RL.7.5

6. What is the poem's theme?

A. Hiking in nature is peaceful.
B. Everyone is confronted by life choices.
C. It is important to forgive others for mistakes.
D. Traveling can be lonely.

CCSS.ELA-LITERACY.RL.7.2

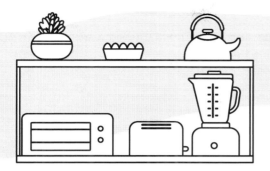

ARGOPREP.COM

VIDEO
EXPLANATIONS ▶

Definition/Explanation Clues

CCSS.ELA-LITERACY.L.7.4.A

Key Terms

What are context clues?

When you read you may come across unfamiliar words. To figure out the meaning of the unfamiliar word, oftentimes you can use context clues. Context clues are words or phrases that act as hints to help you determine the meaning of the unfamiliar word.

What are definition/explanation clues?

One type of context clue is a definition/explanation clue. This is when a definition or explanation of the unfamiliar word is given in the sentence.

Examples

Crampons, **spiked plates worn on boots for climbing on ice and snow**, are necessary for this journey.

The cook brought the colander, **a tool used to drain pasta**, over to the sink.

A gaffer, **the chief electrician on a film set**, works long hours.

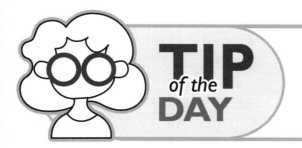
TIP of the DAY

Start looking for definition/explanation clues in passages that you read. Definition/explanation clues are most often found in informational texts.

EXERCISES

Read each sentence and underlined unfamiliar word. In the space provided, write the definition/explanation context clue in each sentence.

1. Nellie was given a rattlesnake bite <u>antidote</u>, medicine for counteracting the effects of poison.

   CCSS.ELA-LITERACY.L.7.4.A

2. Today the ocean looks <u>translucent</u>, completely clear and transparent.

   CCSS.ELA-LITERACY.L.7.4.A

3. Alex's teacher called him <u>gregarious</u>, outgoing and sociable.

   CCSS.ELA-LITERACY.L.7.4.A

4. The rock climber spotted a <u>crevice</u>, a crack forming an opening, on the side of the mountain.

   CCSS.ELA-LITERACY.L.7.4.A

5. We placed a plant <u>specimen</u>, a sample of a substance or material, under the microscope.

   CCSS.ELA-LITERACY.L.7.4.A

6. Jamisha was placed in Honors Math because of her <u>aptitude</u>, intelligence and quickness of learning.

   CCSS.ELA-LITERACY.L.7.4.A

WEEK 12 : WEDNESDAY

Example Clues

CCSS.ELA-LITERACY.L.7.4.A

Key Terms

Let's review context clues. Context clues are words or phrases that act as hints to help you determine the meaning of the unfamiliar word.

What are example clues?

One type of context clue is an example clue. This is when examples of the unfamiliar word are listed in the sentence.

Examples

In the summer I love to eat <u>gelato</u>, such as **chocolate**, **strawberry**, **and cookies and cream**.

<u>Predators</u>, like **mountain lions**, **grizzly bears**, **and gray wolves**, live in the Rocky Mountains.

<u>Astrological signs</u>, including **Capricorn**, **Taurus**, **and Leo**, are said to explain people's personalities.

TIP *of the* **DAY**

While you will use context clues when reading, you can also add them to your own writing to help your readers understand unfamiliar words.

EXERCISES

Read each sentence and underlined unfamiliar word. In the space provided, write the meaning of each unfamiliar word.

---

1. There are many <u>gemstones</u>, such as sapphires, rubies, and jade, that can be discovered in the earth's crust.

   _____

   _____

   CCSS.ELA-LITERACY.L.7.4.A

---

2. Four major <u>eras</u> include Civil War and Reconstruction, the Industrial Age, the Roaring Twenties, and the Great Depression.

   _____

   _____

   CCSS.ELA-LITERACY.L.7.4.A

---

3. <u>Precipitation</u>, like rain, sleet, and snow, has decreased this year.

   _____

   _____

   CCSS.ELA-LITERACY.L.7.4.A

Read each sentence. Use context clues to determine the meaning of each underlined word. Select the best answer.

---

4. Every year there is more <u>debris</u>, such as plastic bags, styrofoam containers, and straws, floating in the ocean.

   A. containers
   B. trash
   C. food
   D. pieces

   CCSS.ELA-LITERACY.L.7.4.A

---

5. Going to college prepares you for many future <u>professions</u>, like nursing, computer programming, and teaching.

   A. classes
   B. topics
   C. technologies
   D. jobs

   CCSS.ELA-LITERACY.L.7.4.A

---

6. <u>Deciduous trees</u>, such as oak, maple, beech, hickory, can be found around New England.

   A. trees that do not lose their leaves
   B. trees that are small
   C. trees that lose their leaves
   D. trees that give fruit

   CCSS.ELA-LITERACY.L.7.4.A

WEEK 12 : FRIDAY

Antonym/Contrast Clues

CCSS.ELA-LITERACY.L.7.4.A

Key Terms

Let's review context clues. Context clues are hints that the author adds to help you figure out the meaning of an unfamiliar word.

What are are antonym/contrast clues?

One type of context clue is an antonym/contrast clue. This is when the opposite meaning of the unfamiliar word is given in the sentence. The contrasting phrase or an antonym will help you figure out the word's meaning. Words such as "unlike," "in contrast," "opposed to," "whereas" are sometimes included to signal the antonym or contrast.

Examples

On Wednesday afternoon, the beach was <u>serene</u>, **versus how loud and crowded it was on Saturday.**

It was a <u>humdrum</u> day, **instead of an exciting and fun day.**

Kyle was feeling <u>peckish</u> **rather than hungry.**

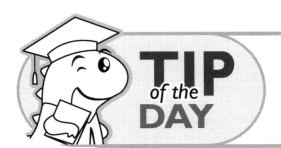

TIP of the **DAY**

Context clues can be given for unfamiliar verbs, nouns, adjectives, or adverbs. Identifying the part of speech will help you understand the meaning of the unfamiliar word.

EXERCISES

Read each sentence and underlined unfamiliar word. In the space provided, write the meaning of the unfamiliar word.

Read each sentence. Use context clues to determine the meaning of each underlined word. Select the best answer.

1. The wedding had a <u>multitude</u> of desserts, instead of one cake.

CCSS.ELA-LITERACY.L.7.4.A

4. Anthony <u>embellished</u> parts of his story for entertainment, rather than tell the full truth.

   A. forgot
   B. retold
   C. shouted
   D. exaggerated

CCSS.ELA-LITERACY.L.7.4.A

2. The end of the movie was <u>somber</u>, versus exciting and heartwarming.

CCSS.ELA-LITERACY.L.7.4.A

5. At the restaurant my sister was <u>civil</u> towards me, instead of quick to start another argument.

   A. rude
   B. polite
   C. unsure
   D. strange

CCSS.ELA-LITERACY.L.7.4.A

3. The students <u>dawdled</u> in the hallway, rather than rush into the classroom.

CCSS.ELA-LITERACY.L.7.4.A

6. Tanner <u>gingerly</u> set down the glass, in contrast to Julie who set hers down hard.

   A. carefully
   B. loudly
   C. clumsily
   D. kindly

CCSS.ELA-LITERACY.L.7.4.A

WEEK 13

VIDEO ► EXPLANATIONS

ARGOPREP.COM

Because I could not stop for Death *by Emily Dickinson*

Because I could not stop for Death –
He kindly stopped for me –
The Carriage held but just Ourselves –
And Immortality.

We slowly drove – He knew no haste
And I had put away
My labor and my leisure too,
For His Civility –

We passed the School, where Children strove
At Recess – in the Ring –
We passed the Fields of Gazing Grain –
We passed the Setting Sun –

Or rather – He passed us –
The Dews drew quivering and chill –
For only Gossamer, my Gown –
My Tippet – only Tulle –

We paused before a House that seemed
A Swelling of the Ground –
The Roof was scarcely visible –
The Cornice – in the Ground –

Since then – 'tis Centuries – and yet
Feels shorter than the Day
I first surmised the Horses' Heads
Were toward Eternity –

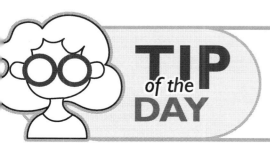

TIP of the DAY

Emily Dickinson uses capital letters and dashes throughout her poem. Poets sometimes use these techniques to draw the reader's attention to specific ideas in the poem.

EXERCISES

1. Which two lines contrast with one another?

   A. "We passed the School, where Children strove/ At Recess – in the Ring –"
   B. "We passed the Fields of Gazing Grain – / We passed the Setting Sun –"
   C. "The Roof was scarcely visible – / The Cornice – in the Ground –"
   D. "Since then – 'tis Centuries – and yet/ Feels shorter than the Day"

   CCSS.ELA-LITERACY.RL.7.4

2. What type of figurative language did the author use throughout the poem? Select the best answer.

   A. simile
   B. idiom
   C. hyperbole
   D. personification

   CCSS.ELA-LITERACY.RL.7.4

3. Select the line from the poem that best supports your answer in question 2.

   A. "He kindly stopped for me – "
   B. "My labor and my leisure too,"
   C. "At Recess – in the Ring – "
   D. "For only Gossamer, my Gown – "

   CCSS.ELA-LITERACY.RL.7.1

4. What does "haste" mean in the line below from stanza 2?

   We slowly drove – He knew no haste

   A. thoughts
   B. miles
   C. speed
   D. answers

   CCSS.ELA-LITERACY.RL.7.4

5. How does the rhythm of the poem impact its meaning?

   A. The rhythm is quick, which contrasts with the theme of death.
   B. The rhythm is similar to the rhythm of a moving horse carriage.
   C. The rhythm changes in the third stanza in order to describe the children playing.
   D. The rhythm repeats, similar to the repeated message of death.

   CCSS.ELA-LITERACY.RL.7.4

6. What type of poem is "Because I could not stop for Death"?

   A. sonnet
   B. haiku
   C. free verse
   D. lyric poem

   CCSS.ELA-LITERACY.RL.7.5

WEEK 13 : WEDNESDAY

Adapted from The Biography of Galileo Galilei *by Albert Van Helden*

Galileo's Early Life

1. Galileo was born in Pisa, Italy on February 15, 1564. His father, Vincenzo Galilei, was a musician, and his mother was named Giulia degli Ammannati. Galileo was the first of six children born into a family of nobility. In the early 1570s, he and his family moved to Florence, Italy.

The Pendulum

2. In 1581 Galileo began studying at the University of Pisa, where his father hoped he would study medicine. While at university, Galileo began his study of the pendulum and, according to legend, he watched a suspended lamp swing back and forth in the cathedral of Pisa. However, it was not until 1602 that Galileo made his most notable discovery about the pendulum — that the period (the time in which a pendulum swings back and forth) does not depend on the arc of the swing (the isochronism). Eventually, this discovery would lead to Galileo's further study of time intervals and the development of his idea for a pendulum clock.

Mechanical Devices

3. In 1592 Galileo was appointed professor of mathematics at the University of Padua. While teaching there, he frequently visited a place called the Arsenal, where Venetian ships were docked and loaded. Galileo had always been interested in mechanical devices. Naturally, during his visits to the Arsenal, he became fascinated by nautical technologies, such as the sector and shipbuilding. In 1593 he was presented with a problem involving the placement of oars in galleys. He treated the oar as a lever and correctly made the water the fulcrum. A year later, he patented a model for a pump. His pump was a device that raised water by using only one horse.

Telescope

4. Galileo invented many mechanical devices other than the pump, such as the hydrostatic balance. But perhaps his most famous invention was the telescope. Galileo made his first telescope in 1609, modeled after telescopes produced in other parts of Europe that could magnify objects three times. He created a telescope later that same year that could magnify objects twenty times. With this telescope, he was able to look at the moon, discover the four satellites of Jupiter, observe a supernova, verify the phases of Venus, and discover sunspots. His discoveries proved the Copernican system which states that the earth and other planets revolve around the sun. Prior to the Copernican system, it was held that the universe was geocentric, meaning the sun revolved around the earth.

The Inquisition

5. Galileo's belief in the Copernican System eventually got him into trouble with the Catholic Church. The Inquisition, a part of the Catholic Church at that time, punished those who went against the teachings of the religion. The astronomer Copernicus proposed that the Sun was the center of the universe. This went against the beliefs of the Catholic Church during this time period. Because Galileo supported the Copernican system, he was warned by Cardinal Bellarmine, under order of Pope Paul V, that he should not discuss or defend Copernican theories. Galileo was able to change the Church's mind. In 1624 Galileo was assured by Pope Urban VIII that he could write about Copernican theory, if he focused on mathematics. However, with the printing of Galileo's book, *Dialogue Concerning the Two Chief World Systems*, Galileo was called to Rome in 1633 to face the Inquisition again. Galileo was found guilty of heresy for writing his book, and he was sent to his home near Florence to be held under house arrest for the remainder of his life. In 1642, Galileo died at his home outside Florence.

TIP
of the
DAY

When you read informational texts, think about the cause and effect relationships between people, events, or ideas.

EXERCISES

1. What does "notable" mean in paragraph 2? Select the best answer.

   A. creative
   B. educated
   C. modern
   D. important

   CCSS.ELA-LITERACY.RI.7.4

2. Based on paragraphs 3-5, which answer choice best describes Galileo?

   A. teacher
   B. inventor
   C. writer
   D. speaker

   CCSS.ELA-LITERACY.RI.7.5

3. Which statement from the passage best supports your answer in question 2?

   A. "In 1592 Galileo was appointed professor of mathematics at the University of Padua."
   B. "While at university, Galileo began his study of the pendulum…"
   C. "While teaching there, he frequently visited a place called the Arsenal, where Venetian ships were docked and loaded."
   D. "But perhaps his most famous invention was the telescope."

   CCSS.ELA-LITERACY.RI.7.1

4. What does "nautical" mean in paragraph 3?

   A. relating to building materials
   B. relating to planets and stars
   C. relating to researching and writing
   D. relating to ships and navigation

   CCSS.ELA-LITERACY.RI.7.4

5. Which word or phrase from the passage best supports the meaning of "nautical"?

   A. "ships were docked"
   B. "mechanical devices"
   C. "presented with a problem"
   D. "using only one horse"

   CCSS.ELA-LITERACY.RI.7.1

6. Which statement communicates a central idea found in paragraph 5?

   A. "The astronomer Copernicus proposed that the Sun was the center of the universe."
   B. "Galileo was able to change the Church's mind."
   C. "Galileo was found guilty of heresy for writing his book, and he was sent to his home near Florence to be held under house arrest for the remainder of his life."
   D. In 1642, Galileo died at his home outside Florence.

   CCSS.ELA-LITERACY.RI.7.2

WEEK 13 : FRIDAY

Adapted from Moby Dick *by Herman Melville*

Moby Dick is a novel about a sailor named Ishmael. In this excerpt of the novel, Ishmael has stayed overnight in an inn and walks downstairs to the bar-room for breakfast.

1. The bar-room was now full of the boarders who had been dropping in the previous night, and whom I had not as yet had a good look at. They were nearly all whalemen: chief mates, and second mates, and third mates, and sea carpenters, and sea coopers, and sea blacksmiths, and harpooneers, and ship keepers. They were a tan and brawny company, with overgrown beards; an unshorn, shaggy set, all wearing their sailing coats instead of robes.

2. You could pretty plainly tell how long each one had been ashore. This young fellow's healthy cheek is like a sun-toasted pear in hue, and would seem to smell almost as musky; he cannot have been three days landed from his Indian voyage. That man next him looks a few shades lighter; you might say a touch of satin wood is in him. In the complexion of a third still lingers a tropical tan, but slightly bleached; he doubtless has tarried whole weeks ashore. Then there was Queequeg, whose skin was like the western slope of the Andes Mountains with contrasting climates in different areas.

3. "Grub, ho!" cried the landlord of the inn, flinging open a door. We all then went in to breakfast.

4. They say that men who have seen the world become quite comfortable around other people. This was not true of everyone, though. For example, Ledyard, the great New England traveller, and Mungo Park, the Scottish man, possessed the least ease in the room. But perhaps Ledyard's crossing of Siberia in a sled drawn by dogs or Mungo's long solitary walk on an empty stomach in Africa were not the best ways to learn social manners.

5. My reflections happened after we were all seated at the table, and I was preparing to hear some good stories about whaling. Nearly every man maintained a profound silence. And not only that, they looked embarrassed. Yes, here was a group of sea-dogs, many of whom had fought great whales on the high seas. Yet, here they sat at a social breakfast table — all of the same calling, all of kindred tastes — looking around sheepishly at each other. A curious sight; these bashful bears, these timid warrior whalemen!

6. But Queequeg sat there among them at the head of the table as cool as an icicle. To be sure I cannot say much for his manners. Even his greatest admirer could not have justified the fact that he brought his whaling harpoon into breakfast with him. He reached over the table with it, to the imminent danger of the other men's heads, and speared the beefsteaks.

7. We will not speak of all of Queequeg's peculiarities here, but he did give his undivided attention to the beefsteaks, done rare, and did not want coffee or hot rolls. When breakfast was over, he withdrew like the rest into the public room. He sat there quietly digesting with his inseparable hat on, and I sallied out for a stroll.

TIP of the DAY

When reading fictional passages, pay attention to the narrator's observations. Those observations can help you understand the setting, other characters, and the plot.

EXERCISES

1. Based on paragraphs 1 and 2, how would you describe the boarders at the inn? Use two details from the passage in your response.

    _____

    _____

    _____

    _____

    CCSS.ELA-LITERACY.RL.7.1

2. Identify an example of figurative language in paragraph 2 and explain its meaning.

    _____

    _____

    _____

    _____

    CCSS.ELA-LITERACY.RL.7.4

3. What does the landlord mean when he shouts, "Grub, ho!," in paragraph 3?

    A. Be quiet!
    B. Leave the inn!
    C. Breakfast is ready!
    D. Help!

    CCSS.ELA-LITERACY.RL.7.4

4. Which statement summarizes paragraphs 4 and 5? Select the best answer.

    A. The men do not like one another.
    B. The men are hungry for breakfast.
    C. The men miss working on the ships.
    D. The men are not sure how to be social.

    CCSS.ELA-LITERACY.RL.7.2

5. Which word from the passage helps you determine the meaning of "harpoon"? Select the best answer.

    A. admirer
    B. reached
    C. speared
    D. beefsteaks

    CCSS.ELA-LITERACY.RL.7.1

6. How does the author contrast Queequeg with the other men?

    A. Queequeg is not a whaleman like the others.
    B. Queequeg is more popular than the others.
    C. Queequeg is angrier than the others.
    D. Queequeg is more confident than the others.

    CCSS.ELA-LITERACY.RL.7.6

WEEK 14

: **VIDEO**
• EXPLANATIONS ▶
ARGOPREP.COM

Greek and Latin Affixes

Key Terms and Examples

The English language contains many Greek and Latin affixes (prefixes and suffixes) and roots. Learning the meanings of these affixes and roots will help you understand new words that you come across when reading.

Today we will look at five prefixes, which are added to the beginnings of roots or base words. Prefixes modify or change a root word's meaning. Read the definitions of each prefix and example below.

ante (Latin): before; in front of

Example: We waited in the antechamber before entering the dining room.

antechamber: a room where a person waits before entering a larger room

ab (Latin): away; from

Example: Sierra was absent from school yesterday.

absent: away from a place at a certain time

con (Latin): with; jointly

Example: The class is studying contemporary poetry.

contemporary: of the same time period; modern

inter (Latin): between two

Example: Jill had a job interview with a restaurant manager.

interview: a formal meeting between two people

intra (Latin): within

The company used an intranet to link their network of computers.

Intranet: a computer network within a company

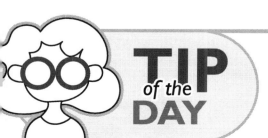

TIP of the DAY

Other languages, such as French and Spanish, also use Greek and Latin roots. The English language includes words that come from those languages as well.

EXERCISES

Read each sentence. Then select the meaning of the underlined word.

1. The family drove on the <u>interstate</u> across Arizona and New Mexico.

   A. a highway that crosses two or more states
   B. a road within one state
   C. a bridge that crosses water
   D. a one-way tunnel

   CCSS.ELA-LITERACY.L.7.4.B

2. We read about the <u>antebellum</u> plantations and then began our unit about the Civil War.

   A. a historical time period
   B. existing before a war
   C. wealthy homes
   D. farms that grow crops

   CCSS.ELA-LITERACY.L.7.4.B

3. The medical test was <u>abnormal</u> for someone so young.

   A. average
   B. expected
   C. not normal
   D. not unique

   CCSS.ELA-LITERACY.L.7.4.B

4. Marissa said, "I <u>concur</u>," when her brother voted for pizza for dinner.

   A. disagree
   B. wish
   C. agree
   D. want

   CCSS.ELA-LITERACY.L.7.4.B

5. Several of the kids in class belong to an <u>intramural</u> soccer team.

   A. involving students from different states
   B. involving teammates from different backgrounds
   C. involving sports played with a ball
   D. involving students at the same school

   CCSS.ELA-LITERACY.L.7.4.B

6. The video game fans attended a game <u>convention</u>.

   A. a speech given by an important leader
   B. a gathering of people with a common interest
   C. a shopping mall with different stores
   D. a demonstration showing a new product

   CCSS.ELA-LITERACY.L.7.4.B

Greek and Latin Roots - Part 1

Key Terms and Examples

cede, ceed (Latin): yield; go, surrender

Example: The announcer told everyone to <u>proceed</u> in the line.

proceed: go forward

chron (Greek): time

Example: The history chapter was arranged in <u>chronological</u> order.

chronological: time order

temp (Latin): time

Example: The cast on my arm is only <u>temporary</u> until the break heals.

temporary: lasting for only a time; not permanent

mot/mob (Latin): to move

Example: The car's <u>motor</u> was loud in traffic.

motor: an engine that allows a car to move

fract/frag (Latin): to break

Example: The pizza slices were a <u>fraction</u> of the entire pie.

fraction: a part of a whole; a section

TIP of the DAY

When you read a text, circle, highlight, or underline unfamiliar words. Identify any context clues that may help you understand the unfamiliar word.

127

EXERCISES

Read each sentence. Then select the meaning of the underlined word.

1. The boy tripped on the basketball court and <u>fractured</u> his wrist.

   A. sprained
   B. broke
   C. hurt
   D. bent

   CCSS.ELA-LITERACY.L.7.4.B

2. The band needed to work on the song's <u>tempo</u>.

   A. melody
   B. sound
   C. notes
   D. timing

   CCSS.ELA-LITERACY.L.7.4.B

3. We have to stop the test because we have <u>exceeded</u> the time limit.

   A. gone beyond
   B. not finished
   C. stopped
   D. forgotten

   CCSS.ELA-LITERACY.L.7.4.B

4. The dancers were <u>synchronized</u> during the routine.

   A. elegant and graceful
   B. confused throughout
   C. moving at the same time
   D. standing in line

   CCSS.ELA-LITERACY.L.7.4.B

5. The mirror fell, leaving <u>fragments</u> of glass on the floor.

   A. sharp items
   B. dangerous bits
   C. broken pieces
   D. shiny objects

   CCSS.ELA-LITERACY.L.7.4.B

6. After being sick in bed for days, Melanie is <u>mobile</u> again.

   A. capable of moving
   B. healthy
   C. exhausted and ill
   D. stuck in one place

   CCSS.ELA-LITERACY.L.7.4.B

Greek and Latin Roots - Part 2

Key Terms and Examples

gen: species, kind, race

Example: My mom is using <u>genealogy</u> to learn about her family and ancestors.

genealogy: the study of family history

mater, matr (Latin): mother

Example: The dog showed her <u>maternal</u> instinct when she licked and protected the kitten.

maternal: relating to motherhood

opt (Latin): eye

Example: Kayla had an eye exam at the <u>optometrist's</u> office.

optometrist: an eye doctor

pater, patr (Latin): father

Example: My <u>paternal</u> grandfather is my dad's father.

paternal: relating to fatherhood

ped/pod: foot

Example: My little sister learned how to use the <u>pedals</u> on her bike.

pedal: a bicycle lever that is operated by the foot

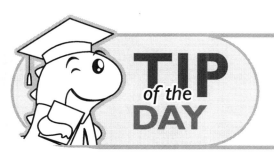

TIP of the DAY

As you learn more Greek and Latin roots and affixes, you'll be able to break down parts of challenging words. Many words you come across science and history will have Greek and Latin roots and affixes.

Read each sentence. Then select the meaning of the underlined word.

1. We stared at the <u>optical</u> illusion on the computer screen.

   A. relating to a puzzle
   B. relating to sounds
   C. relating to sight or vision
   D. relating to one or more

   CCSS.ELA-LITERACY.L.7.4.B

2. My parents' <u>generation</u> did not have cell phones when they were young.

   A. a family with many cousins
   B. people born in the same time period
   C. university or college
   D. grandparents

   CCSS.ELA-LITERACY.L.7.4.B

3. The <u>matriarch</u> was a lawyer and had three children.

   A. female head of a family
   B. professional in the legal field
   C. a parent who works
   D. leader of a family

   CCSS.ELA-LITERACY.L.7.4.B

4. When Phil broke his foot, he visited a <u>podiatrist</u> and got an X-ray.

   A. X-ray specialist
   B. foot doctor
   C. pharmacy
   D. family doctor

   CCSS.ELA-LITERACY.L.7.4.B

5. James took <u>paternity</u> leave from work after his baby was born.

   A. relating to fatherhood
   B. relating to a job or career
   C. relating to babies
   D. relating to brotherhood

   CCSS.ELA-LITERACY.L.7.4.B

6. In science we learned that eye color is determined through <u>genetics</u>.

   A. chance or luck
   B. the study of science
   C. calculating the probability
   D. passing traits from parents to children

   CCSS.ELA-LITERACY.L.7.4.B

WEEK 15

Adapted from Oliver Twist *by Charles Dickens*

Oliver Twist is about a boy who is an orphan, or does not have any family. This excerpt of the novel describes Oliver's life in a workhouse, a place where poor people lived and worked in London, England in the 1800s.

1. The room in which the boys were fed, was a large stone hall, with a large heated copper pot at one end: out of which the master, dressed in an apron for the purpose, and assisted by one or two women, ladled the gruel at meal-times. Each boy could have one bowl, and no more — except on occasions of holidays, when they had two ounces and also a quarter of bread. The bowls never wanted washing. The boys polished them with their spoons till they shone again. When they had performed this operation (which never took very long, the spoons being nearly as large as the bowls), they would sit staring at the copper pot. They had such eager eyes, it was as if they could have devoured the very bricks of which it sat. In the meantime, they sucked their fingers most assiduously, with the view of catching up any stray splashes of gruel that might have been left. Boys have generally excellent appetites.

2. Oliver Twist and his companions suffered the tortures of slow starvation for three months: at last they got so voracious and wild with hunger. One boy, who was tall for his age, and hadn't been used to that sort of thing (for his father had kept a small cookshop), hinted darkly to his companions. He said that unless he had another bowl of gruel every day, he was afraid he might eat the boy who slept next to him some night. He had a wild hungry eye; and they believed him. The boys decided to vote on who should walk up to the master after supper that evening and ask for more; and it fell to Oliver Twist.

3. The evening arrived; the boys took their places. The master, in his cook's uniform, stationed himself at the copper pot. His pauper assistants stood behind him. The gruel was served, and a long prayer was said for mealtime. Once all of the gruel was gone, some of the boys whispered to each other and winked at Oliver, while his neighbors nudged him. Child as he was, he was desperate with hunger, and reckless with misery. He rose from the table, and walked toward the master, bowl and spoon in hand. He then said, somewhat alarmed at his own boldness:

4. "Please, sir, I want some more."

5. The master was a fat, healthy man, but he turned very pale. He gazed in astonishment at the small rebel for a long time, and then clung to the copper pot for support. The assistants were paralyzed with wonder; the boys with fear.

6. "What!" said the master at length, in a faint voice.

7. "Please, sir," replied Oliver, "I want some more."

8. The master aimed a blow at Oliver's head with the ladle, grabbed his arms, and shrieked aloud for Mr. Bumble. After he told him what had happened, Mr. Bumble went straight to the head of the workhouse, Mr. Limbkins.

9. Mr. Bumble rushed into the room in great excitement, and said, "Mr. Limbkins, I beg your pardon, sir! Oliver Twist has asked for more!"

10. He was startled, his face filled with horror.

11. "For more!" said Mr. Limbkins. "Compose yourself, Bumble, and answer me distinctly. Do I understand that he asked for more, after he had eaten the supper given to him?"

12. "He did, sir," replied Bumble.

13. "That boy will be in prison someday," said the gentleman in the white waistcoat. "I know that boy will be in prison."

14. Nobody disagreed with him at that moment. An animated discussion took place. Oliver was ordered into instant confinement, where he could not speak to the other boys. The next morning a bill was pasted on the outside of the gate, offering a reward of five pounds to anybody who would take Oliver Twist off the hands of the workhouse. In other words, five pounds and Oliver Twist was offered to any man or woman who wanted an apprentice to any trade, business, or calling.

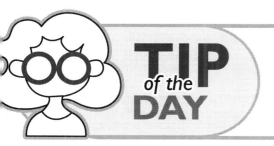

TIP of the DAY

Have you noticed how authors write characters' dialogue? When you are writing your own narratives, start a new paragraph each time you switch between different characters' dialogue.

EXERCISES

1. In paragraph 1, why did the narrator state that the bowls never needed washing?

   A. The bowls were used only once and then thrown out.
   B. The boys were so hungry that they licked the bowls clean.
   C. The boys were forced to wash the bowls themselves.
   D. The workhouse did not care if the boys had clean bowls or not.

   CCSS.ELA-LITERACY.RL.7.3

2. What does assiduously mean in paragraph 1?

   A. painfully; sorely
   B. lightly; slightly
   C. thoroughly; completely
   D. quietly; secretly

   CCSS.ELA-LITERACY.RL.7.4

3. How does paragraph 2 impact the story? Select the best answer.

   A. Paragraph 2 sets up the conflict in the story.
   B. Paragraph 2 introduces the setting in the story.
   C. Paragraph 2 solves the problem in the story.
   D. Paragraph 2 teaches the lesson in the story.

   CCSS.ELA-LITERACY.RL.7.3

4. What surprised Oliver in paragraphs 3 and 4?

   A. Oliver was surprised that there was no food left.
   B. Oliver was surprised that the boys chose him to walk up to the master.
   C. Oliver was surprised by his boldness to ask for more food.
   D. Oliver was surprised by the master's reaction to his question.

   CCSS.ELA-LITERACY.RL.7.1

5. Which detail best reveals what surprised the adults in the story?

   A. "'Compose yourself, Bumble, and answer me distinctly.'"
   B. "'Do I understand that he asked for more, after he had eaten the supper given to him?'"
   C. "'He did, sir.'"
   D. "'That boy will be in prison someday... I know that boy will be in prison.'"

   CCSS.ELA-LITERACY.RL.7.1

6. Which statement best summarizes paragraph 14?

   A. The workhouse wants Oliver to learn a trade and work with an apprentice.
   B. Oliver could no longer speak with the other boys who got him in trouble.
   C. The workhouse offered five pounds to anyone who would take Oliver.
   D. The workhouse no longer wants to take care of Oliver, and he was punished.

   CCSS.ELA-LITERACY.RL.7.2

134

A Birthday *by Christina Rossetti*

My heart is like a singing bird
  Whose nest is in a water'd shoot;
My heart is like an apple-tree
  Whose boughs are bent with thick-set fruit;
My heart is like a rainbow shell
  That paddles in a halcyon sea;
My heart is gladder than all these,
  Because my love is come to me.

Raise me a daïs of silk and down;
  Hang it with vair and purple dyes;
Carve it in doves and pomegranates,
  And peacocks with a hundred eyes;
Work it in gold and silver grapes,
  In leaves and silver fleurs-de-lys;
Because the birthday of my life
  Is come, my love is come to me.

TIP of the DAY

Stanzas are similar to paragraphs in stories. Each stanza has its own central idea. Think about the main idea of each stanza to help you understand the overall meaning of a poem.

EXERCISES

1. What is the meaning of the following lines from the first stanza?

   My heart is like an apple-tree
   Whose boughs are bent with thick-set fruit

   A. The speaker is full of happiness.
   B. The speaker's heart is heavy.
   C. The speaker's favorite fruit is an apple.
   D. The speaker lives near an apple orchard.

2. What is the rhyme scheme of the first stanza?

   A. ABABDCEC
   B. ABCBDCAC
   C. ABCDABCD
   D. ABCBDCEC

3. The author uses repetition in the first stanza. How does this impact the poem?

   A. The phrase "my heart" is repeated, which relates to the speaker's broken heart.
   B. The phrase "my heart" is repeated to emphasize the theme of love.
   C. The phrase "my heart" is repeated in order to create conflict in the poem.
   D. The phrase "my heart" is repeated to describe the speaker's personality.

4. Which type of figurative language is used in the first six lines of the poem?

   A. onomatopoeia
   B. simile
   C. allusion
   D. metaphor

5. The author mentions several colors throughout the poem. How does this impact the poem?

   A. The colors help showcase the dark conflict in the poem.
   B. The colors describe the setting in the poem.
   C. They create a confusing story throughout the poem.
   D. The colors create a joyful tone in the poem.

6. What season does the poem represent?

   A. winter
   B. spring
   C. summer
   D. fall

Adapted from Scott Joplin *by Catherine Schmidt-Jones*

Introduction

1. Scott Joplin is the undisputed "King of Ragtime" music. Many composers published piano rags and other ragtime music around the turn of the twentieth century. But it was the music of Scott Joplin that really captured the public's attention, both then and during ragtime's revival in the second half of the century. The widespread popularity of Joplin's music during his lifetime was one of the first steps on the long road that led to widespread recognition of African-American music, particularly jazz, as an important, influential, and serious art.

Background

2. When Scott Joplin was born, the Civil War had recently freed slaves in the U.S., but almost a century would pass before the arrival of the Civil Rights movement. It would be hard to overestimate the effect this had on Joplin's life and music. Scott Joplin inhabited a world in which a black man's career choices were basically limited to preacher, teacher, musician, or poorly paid manual laborer. A black musician was not welcome in a concert hall or many other venues where only white musicians were considered acceptable.

3. The music of Joplin's world came from both Europe and Africa, and, like ragtime itself, Joplin was strongly influenced by both. He probably learned the basics of European classical music from Julius Weiss, a neighbor who was so impressed with young Scott's talent that he offered him music lessons.

4. But the young Scott Joplin would also have heard, at home, at church, and in nearby fields and saloons, the music of his newly-freed people: spirituals, work "hollers," plantation songs, and "patting Juba."

5. The influence of both can be clearly heard in all ragtime music, and it is the fusion of the two traditions that give ragtime, and indeed all the jazz traditions that would later follow, their tremendous energy. In the case of the classic piano rag, the European influence can be seen most clearly in the form of the music, which generally follows the outline of a march, with its repeated stanzas and trio sections. The steady "boom-chick" of the bass is also very march-like. The most obvious contribution of the African influence is the syncopated rhythms which make ragtime so easily recognizable.

Biography

6. Nobody can say with certainty when or where Scott Joplin was born. The best information available seems to point to northeast Texas in 1867 or 1868. He grew up near Texarkana. His parents were ex-slave Jiles Joplin and free-born African-American Florence Givens. Jiles and Florence were both musicians. He played the violin, she played banjo and sang, and five of their six children also sang or played instruments. Scott's talents, in particular, were apparent at an early age.

7. He started travelling while still quite young, making a living as an itinerant pianist, and as a vocalist with the Texas Medley Quartette, which included two of his brothers. Eventually, around 1885, he settled in St. Louis, Missouri, the famous "Gateway to the West" that was a major center for rail and riverboat travel. He worked as a pianist at the Silver Dollar Saloon, but he also continued to travel and perform extensively. In 1893 he moved to Chicago, where he organized his first band, played cornet, and met Otis Saunders, another rag pianist. Saunders encouraged him to write down and publish the piano compositions he had been improvising.

8. In 1894 Joplin and Saunders left Chicago, traveling the midwest again, back to St. Louis and eventually to Sedalia, Missouri, where Joplin settled by 1896. There he composed, taught, organized another band, and played piano in clubs. He named his second published piece for a Sedalia club, the Maple Leaf. Published in 1899, Maple Leaf Rag became a big hit, not only all over the United States, but in Europe as well. Now established as a popular and famous composer, Joplin continued to travel widely, but also spent much time composing. Around 1900 he moved back to St. Louis. Around the same time, he also married Belle Hayden, the sister-in-law of one of his students. They separated, however, and a second marriage in 1904, to Freddie Alexander, ended after only a few weeks when his bride died of pneumonia.

9. Joplin moved to New York City in 1907, and in 1909 married Lottie Stokes. Until his move to New York, Joplin had published a fairly steady stream of piano rags, as well as a few longer works such as a ragtime opera entitled *A Guest of Honor*. He was driven by the desire to be considered a "serious" composer, though, so he began to devote much of his time to his second opera, *Treemonisha*.

10. *Treemonisha* was not a ragtime opera, although it did include a few numbers in ragtime style. Joplin's aim was to write a serious opera which included musical references to all types of African-American music, including blues. The message of the opera is that black people can free themselves through education. But Joplin may have been too far ahead of his time. Even African-Americans could not accept the idea of "serious" music written in a style that was normally found in saloons. The production in 1915 of *Treemonisha* was a failure. This was a severe blow to Joplin, who was already ill and had been showing signs of mental strain.

11. In 1916 Scott Joplin was committed to the Manhattan State Hospital, where he died on April 1, 1917. His music faded from popularity as other musical crazes replaced ragtime, and his genius as a composer was not generally recognized until a revival of ragtime led to the widespread rediscovery of his music in the 1970s. In 1976 Joplin at last received the recognition he had always wanted; *Treemonisha* was awarded a special Pulitzer Prize.

TIP of the DAY

When you read an informational text about history, think about why the person or event is important to history. Did the person or event affect other people or events?

EXERCISES

1. Describe ragtime music. Use two details from the passage in your response.

CCSS.ELA-LITERACY.RI.7.1

3. What is the main purpose of paragraph 6 in the passage?

A. It helps explain why Joplin was a natural musician.
B. It provides details about Joplin's birthplace.
C. It describes when Joplin was born.
D. It identifies his parents' names.

CCSS.ELA-LITERACY.RI.7.8

2. What is the author's point of view in paragraph 2?

CCSS.ELA-LITERACY.RI.7.6

4. Which detail from the passage best explains how Joplin became a popular composer?

A. "There he composed, taught, organized another band, and played piano in clubs."
B. "Published in 1899, Maple Leaf Rag became a big hit, not only all over the United States, but in Europe as well."
C. "Joplin moved to New York City in 1907, and in 1909 married Lottie Stokes."
D. "He was driven by the desire to be considered a "serious" composer, though, so he began to devote much of his time to his second opera, *Treemonisha*."

CCSS.ELA-LITERACY.RI.7.1

EXERCISES

5. What is the meaning of "This was a severe blow to Joplin" in paragraph 10?

    A. *Treemonisha* cost Joplin a great deal of money, and it put him in debt.
    B. Joplin was sick, and he needed to go to the hospital.
    C. The opera was a failure, and it was a painful shock to him.
    D. Joplin was mentally exhausted, and he needed a break.

    CCSS.ELA-LITERACY.RI.7.4

6. What are the contrasting ideas in paragraph 11?

    A. Joplin was committed to the Manhattan State Hospital, and he died a year later.
    B. Joplin's talent as a composer was not respected until his music was rediscovered in the 1970s.
    C. A revival of ragtime music occurred in the 1970s, and Joplin's opera received a Pulitzer Prize.
    D. Joplin died in 1917, and ragtime music faded from popularity.

    CCSS.ELA-LITERACY.RI.7.2

NOTES

Allusions

CCSS.ELA-LITERACY.L.7.5.A

<u>Key Terms and Examples</u>

What are allusions?

Many phrases or words that we use in conversation or come across when reading are allusions. Allusions are references or mentions of a person, place, thing, or idea in literature or history.

Allusions are often made to characters in Greek mythology or classic literature, biblical references, or figures in history.

The following are examples of sentences with allusions.

The painter's wife was also his **muse**, and he constantly painted pictures that included her.

This example comes from Greek mythology. Muses were minor goddesses in Greek mythology and gave others creative inspiration.

Jack can be such a **Jekyll and Hyde**; one moment he's nice to me, and the next moment he's mean.

This example comes from the book *The Strange Case of Dr. Jekyll and Mr. Hyde* about a man with two sides (bad and good) to his personality.

My little sister is such a **Judas** for telling on me.

This example is a biblical reference. In the Bible, Judas was considered a traitor.

Congress **stonewalled** the proposed bill.

This example is from U.S. history. Thomas "Stonewall" Jackson was a confederate general during the Civil War. His famous nickname came from another general who supposedly said, "There is Jackson standing like a stone wall! Rally behind the Virginians!" The allusion "stonewall" means to block.

TIP *of the* **DAY**

You can use the Internet to research other examples of allusions from mythology, literature, the Bible, or history.

EXERCISES

Read each selection. In the space provided, write the portion of the selection that includes an allusion.

---

1. His Achilles' heel is multiplying fractions; he needs to keep practicing.

   CCSS.ELA-LITERACY.L.7.5.A

2. My brother is such a Scrooge about putting up Christmas decorations, but the rest of us love it.

   CCSS.ELA-LITERACY.L.7.5.A

3. Americans must pay Uncle Sam taxes.

   CCSS.ELA-LITERACY.L.7.5.A

4. You're going to open a Pandora's box if you cheat on the test.

   CCSS.ELA-LITERACY.L.7.5.A

5. Jessica's dog is a Goliath compared to Maggie's chihuahua.

   CCSS.ELA-LITERACY.L.7.5.A

6. Tony is such a Casanova around girls, and quite a few have a crush on him.

   CCSS.ELA-LITERACY.L.7.5.A

Hyperbole

CCSS.ELA-LITERACY.L.7.5.A

<u>Key Terms and Examples</u>

What is hyperbole?

Hyperbole is a figure of speech used by writers. It is a statement that uses extreme exaggeration to make a point. Many examples of hyperbole can be found in literature.

Here is an example from Babe the Blue Ox, a Paul Bunyan folktale:

"Well now, one winter it was so cold that all the geese flew backward and all the fish moved south and even the snow turned blue. Late at night, it got so frigid that all spoken words froze solid before they could be heard. People had to wait until sun-up to find out what folks were talking about the night before."

In this example of hyperbole, exaggeration is used to describe how cold the winter was. In reality, we know that geese cannot fly backward and fish cannot move south like birds. Snow cannot actually turn blue from cold temperatures, and our words spoken out loud can't freeze solid. The hyperbole creatively communicates the message about the cold winter weather to the reader, though.

Here is another example from "The Tell-Tale Heart: by Edgar Allen Poe:

"TRUE! — nervous — very, very dreadfully nervous I had been and am; but why will you say that I am mad? The disease had sharpened my senses — not destroyed — not dulled them. Above all was the sense of hearing acute. I heard all things in the heaven and in the earth. I heard many things in hell. How, then, am I mad? Hearken! and observe how healthily — how calmly I can tell you the whole story."

In this example of hyperbole, the narrator uses exaggeration when he says that he heard "all the things in the heaven and in the earth." It is not possible for a person to hear all things, but the narrator is using exaggeration to describe just how good his hearing was.

TIP of the DAY

People often use hyperbole in every day conversations. Listen for examples of hyperbole when you talk to your family and friends.

EXERCISES

Read each selection. In the space provided, write the portion of the selection that showcases hyperbole.

1. Max was so hungry he could eat an entire Thanksgiving turkey.

    CCSS.ELA-LITERACY.L.7.5.A

2. Deja's chemistry book weighed a ton.

    CCSS.ELA-LITERACY.L.7.5.A

3. We waited in line for two hours — an eternity — to meet our favorite singer.

    CCSS.ELA-LITERACY.L.7.5.A

4. I died from embarrassment when my voice cracked during the song.

    CCSS.ELA-LITERACY.L.7.5.A

5. Kendra is so tall that she reaches the clouds!

    CCSS.ELA-LITERACY.L.7.5.A

6. There are a million reasons to exercise throughout the week.

    CCSS.ELA-LITERACY.L.7.5.A

WEEK 16 : FRIDAY

Metaphors and Similes

CCSS.ELA-LITERACY.L.7.5.A

Key Terms and Examples

What are metaphors and similes?

Let's review metaphors and similes. Metaphors and similes are figures of speech that use comparison. Writers use metaphors and similes to add variety to their writing. Figures of speech are not meant to be taken literally, so when you come across a metaphor or simile, think about why the author is comparing the two things. What is the meaning behind the comparison?

What is the difference between metaphors and similes?

The difference between these figures of speech is that similes use a signal word, such as "like" or "as" to make the comparison.

Here is an example from Shakespeare's play Romeo and Juliet:

> ROMEO: But, soft! what light through yonder window breaks?
> It is the east, and Juliet is the sun.

Shakespeare includes a metaphor by comparing the character Juliet to the sun. When Romeo says this in the play, he is emphasizing that Juliet is a bright and positive part of his life (in fact, he is in love with her).

The following example is from the poem "Hope" by Emily Dickinson.

> "Hope is the thing with feathers
> That perches in the soul,
> And sings the tune without the words,
> And never stops at all."

Dickinson compares the feeling of hope to a bird. We know this because of words such as "feathers," "perches" and "sings." She is making the point that having hope is beautiful like a singing bird.

The last example is a simile from the poem "A Red, Red Rose" by Robert Burns:

> "O my Luve's like a red, red rose
> That's newly sprung in June;"

The author includes a simile in this example. The simile compares his love to a red rose. He uses "like" to make the comparison. The simile explains that the person he loves is as wonderful as a red rose that has just bloomed.

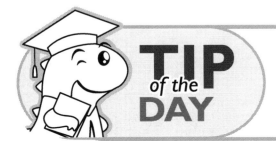

You can add similes and metaphors to your own writing to add variety or emphasize an idea. Be creative!

146

EXERCISES

Read each selection. Then choose the correct meaning of the metaphor or simile.

1. From Shakespeare's play *As You Like It*:

   "All the world's a stage,
   And all the men and women merely players."

   A. Some people pursue acting as a career.
   B. There are many people across the world.
   C. Life has conflict and drama, just like a play.
   D. Shakespeare was more famous than the actors in his plays.

   CCSS.ELA-LITERACY.L.7.5.A

2. From the novel *The Red Badge of Courage* by Stephen Crane:

   "In the eastern sky there was a yellow patch like a rug laid for the feet of the coming sun..."

   A. The sun is rising in the sky.
   B. The rug is yellow like the sun.
   C. The sun is setting in the sky.
   D. A patch in the rug looks worn.

   CCSS.ELA-LITERACY.L.7.5.A

3. From the novel *Little Women* by Louisa May Alcott:

   "...she tried to get rid of the kitten which had scrambled up her back and stuck like a burr just out of reach."

   A. The kitten wanted to cuddle with her.
   B. The kitten was using its claws to hang on her back.
   C. The kitten was soft and fluffy.
   D. The kitten was a baby and could not control itself.

   CCSS.ELA-LITERACY.L.7.5.A

4. From the story *The Adventure of the Three Gables*, by Sir Arthur Conan Doyle:

   "She entered with ungainly struggle like some huge awkward chicken, torn, squawking, out of its coop."

   A. She was a large woman.
   B. She walked in clumsily and noisily.
   C. She was fighting with someone.
   D. She was nervous.

   CCSS.ELA-LITERACY.L.7.5.A

5. From the poem "The Birches" by Robert Frost:

   "And life is too much like a pathless wood / Where your face burns and tickles with the cobwebs"

   A. Woods have many bugs like spiders.
   B. Life is often confusing.
   C. Walking into a cobweb is irritating.
   D. The woods did not have a path for walking.

   CCSS.ELA-LITERACY.L.7.5.A

6. From the poem "Epipsychidion" by Percy Bysshe Shelley:

   "And how my soul was as a lampless sea"

   A. The moon was not shining.
   B. The narrator is a sailor.
   C. There was a storm over the sea.
   D. The narrator felt dark inside.

   CCSS.ELA-LITERACY.L.7.5.A

NOTES

WEEK 17

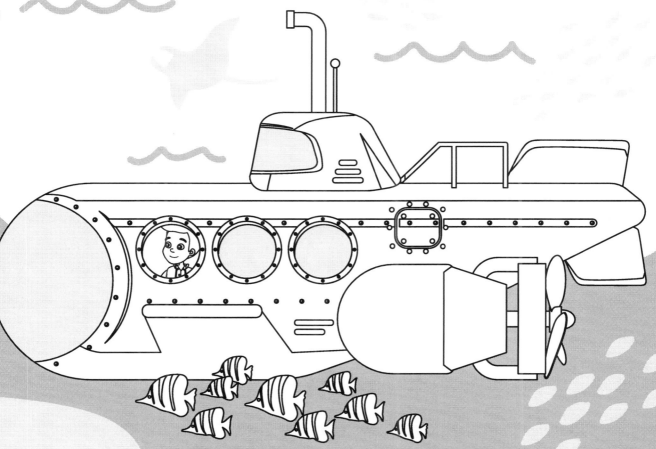

Adapted from Twenty Thousand Leagues Under the Sea *by Jules Verne*

1. Captain Nemo stood up. I followed him. Contrived at the rear of the dining room, a double door opened, and I entered a room whose dimensions equaled the one I had just left.

2. It was a library. Tall, black–rosewood bookcases, inlaid with copper, held on their wide shelves a large number of uniformly bound books. These furnishings followed the contours of the room, their lower parts leading to huge couches upholstered in maroon leather and curved for maximum comfort. Light, movable reading stands, which could be pushed away or pulled near as desired, allowed books to be positioned on them for easy study. In the center stood a huge table covered with pamphlets, among which some newspapers, long out of date, were visible. Electric light flooded this whole harmonious totality, falling from four frosted half globes set in the scrollwork of the ceiling. I stared in genuine wonderment at this room so ingeniously laid out, and I couldn't believe my eyes.

3. "Captain Nemo," I told my host, who had just stretched out on a couch, "this is a library that would do credit to more than one continental palace, and I truly marvel to think it can go with you into the deepest seas."

4. "Where could one find greater silence or solitude, professor?" Captain Nemo replied. "Did your study at the museum afford you such a perfect retreat?"

5. "No, sir, and I might add that it's quite a humble one next to yours. You own 6,000 or 7,000 volumes here…"

6. "12,000, Professor Aronnax. They're my sole remaining ties with dry land. But I was done with the shore the day my Nautilus submerged for the first time under the waters. That day I purchased my last volumes, my last pamphlets, my last newspapers, and ever since I've chosen to believe that humanity no longer thinks or writes. In any event, professor, these books are at your disposal, and you may use them freely."

7. I thanked Captain Nemo and approached the shelves of this library. Written in every language, books on science, ethics, and literature were there in abundance, but I didn't see a single work on economics — they seemed to be strictly banned on board. One odd detail: all these books were shelved indiscriminately without regard to the language in which they were written, and this jumble proved that the Nautilus's captain could read fluently whatever volumes he chanced to pick up. Among these books I noted masterpieces by the greats of ancient and modern times, in other words, all of humanity's finest achievements in history, poetry, fiction, and science.

8. "Sir," I told the captain, "thank you for placing this library at my disposal. There are scientific treasures here, and I'll take advantage of them."

9. Just then Captain Nemo opened a door facing the one by which I had entered the library, and I passed into an immense, splendidly lit lounge.

10. It was a huge quadrilateral with canted corners, ten meters long, six wide, five high. A luminous ceiling, decorated with delicate arabesques, distributed a soft, clear daylight over all the wonders gathered in this museum. For a museum it truly was, in which clever hands had spared no expense to amass every natural and artistic treasures, displaying them with the helter-skelter picturesqueness that distinguishes a painter's studio.

11. Some thirty pictures by the masters, uniformly framed and separated by gleaming panoplies of arms, adorned walls on which were stretched tapestries of austere design. There I saw canvases of the highest value, the likes of which I had marveled at in private European collections and art exhibitions. As the Nautilus's commander had predicted, my mind was already starting to fall into that promised state of stunned amazement.

12. "Professor," this strange man then said, "you must excuse the informality with which I receive you, and the disorder reigning in this lounge."

13. "Sir," I replied, "without prying into who you are, might I venture to identify you as an artist?"

14. "A collector, sir, nothing more. Formerly I loved acquiring these beautiful works created by the hand of man. I sought them greedily, ferreted them out tirelessly, and I've been able to gather some objects of great value. They're my last mementos of those shores that are now dead for me. In my eyes, your modern artists are already as old as the ancients. They've existed for 2,000 or 3,000 years, and I mix them up in my mind. The masters are ageless."

15. "What about these composers?" I said, pointing to sheet music by Weber, Rossini, Mozart, Beethoven, Haydn, Meyerbeer, Hérold, Wagner, Auber, Gounod, Victor Massé, and a number of others scattered over a full size piano-organ, which occupied one of the wall panels in this lounge.

16. "These composers," Captain Nemo answered me, "are the contemporaries of Orpheus, because in the annals of the dead, all chronological differences fade; and I'm dead, professor, quite as dead as those friends of yours sleeping six feet under!"

17. Captain Nemo fell silent and seemed lost in reverie. I regarded him with intense excitement, silently analyzing his strange facial expression. Leaning his elbow on the corner of a valuable mosaic table, he no longer saw me, he had forgotten my very presence.

TIP of the DAY

When you are reading a fictional narrative, compare and contrast the characters. Use descriptions of the characters and their dialogue to figure out how they are similar and different.

EXERCISES

1. What does the following statement from paragraph 1 mean? Select the best answer.

   ...I entered a room whose dimensions equaled the one I had just left.

   A. The second room had the same furniture as the first.
   B. The second room was smaller than the first.
   C. The second room was colder than the first.
   D. The second room was the same size as the first.

   CCSS.ELA-LITERACY.RL.7.4

2. What type of literary device does the author use in paragraph 2?

   A. imagery
   B. personification
   C. simile
   D. metaphor

   CCSS.ELA-LITERACY.RL.7.4

3. What does the word "humble" mean as it is used in paragraph 5?

   A. more academic
   B. more expensive
   C. smaller in size
   D. less interesting

   CCSS.ELA-LITERACY.RL.7.4

4. Looking through the library, what does the professor determine about the captain?

   A. The captain does not know how to read.
   B. The captain understood multiple languages.
   C. The captain wanted to become a professor.
   D. The captain wants to return to dry land.

   CCSS.ELA-LITERACY.RL.7.2

EXERCISES

5. Which detail from the passage best supports your answer from question 4?

A. "12,000, Professor Aronnax. They're my sole remaining ties with dry land."

B. "I didn't see a single work on economics — they seemed to be strictly banned on board..."

C. "...all these books were shelved indiscriminately without regard to the language in which they were written."

D. "Among these books I noted masterpieces by the greats of ancient and modern times..."

CCSS.ELA-LITERACY.RL.7.1

6. Which statement summarizes paragraph 17? Select the best answer.

A. The captain is physically ill.
B. The captain disagrees with the professor.
C. The captain becomes lost in thought.
D. The captain loves music.

CCSS.ELA-LITERACY.RL.7.2

NOTES

Adapted from Flutes *by Catherine Schmidt-Jones*

Introduction

1. A flute is an aerophone that is played by blowing air across a sharp edge in the mouthpiece of the instrument. The flute family is a large family of instruments that includes widely-recognized instruments such as the orchestral flute and piccolo, panpipes, and recorders, as well as unusual instruments such as nose flutes and ocarinas. Although many particular kinds of flutes are not widely known, flutes in general are probably the most common non-percussion instrument found in music traditions around the world.

2. Flutes are usually (but not always) long, thin cylinders that are open at both ends. (Even if the flute appears to be closed at the mouthpiece end, air can usually escape at the blowhole, making the flute effectively an open-open cylindrical tube instrument.) If the player blows into one end of the cylinder, the flute is called end-blown; if the blow hole is on the side of the instrument, it is side-blown, or transverse. Flutes that are not cylindrical (such as ocarinas) are usually classified as vessel flutes.

Flute Mouthpieces

3. There are many different types of flutes played around the world. Some have keys, some just finger holes, some are a collection of tubes, and some are just whistles. The one thing that classifies an instrument as a flute is the mouthpiece, where the sound originates.

4. Flutes have a sharp edge mouthpiece. The sound is produced by blowing a thin, concentrated stream of air at a sharp edge. The stream of air, instead of splitting smoothly at the sharp edge, vibrates back and forth between one side of the edge and the other. This vibration is picked up, reinforced, and turned into a pretty sound by the rest of the instrument.

5. The two major families of flutes are the blow hole aerophones, in which the mouth must direct the air stream toward one edge of a blowhole, and the whistle mouthpiece aerophones, in which the player blows into a whistle-type mouthpiece that directs the air toward a sharp edge.

The Orchestral Flute

6. The flute most commonly used in today's Western orchestras and bands is a side-blown, or transverse flute made of metal (or sometimes dark wood). It is a concert-pitch (non-transposing) instrument. Its basic design — particularly its system of keys and fingerings — was developed by Theobald Boehm (1793-1881) of Munich, in the 1830's. Boehm was a concert flautist (flute player), and also a goldsmith who had some understanding of acoustics (the physics of sound). He changed the placement of the finger holes, enlarged them, and added complex keywork mounted on rods along the body of the instrument. Boehm's design was a distinct improvement on earlier instruments, and the flute is now the most agile of the orchestral woodwinds. The orchestral flute has a cylindrical bore. Its timbre is dominated by the fundamental harmonic, giving it a very clear, uncomplicated sound.

7. The flute can usually be disassembled into three sections: the head joint (which includes the mouthpiece), the middle joint, and the foot joint. It has sixteen keys padded with felt to ensure an airtight seal when the key is held down by a finger. When at rest, the key is held open by a small steel spring.

Piccolo and Alto Flutes

8. Two other flutes sometimes found in Western music are the piccolo and alto flutes. The flauto piccolo (Italian for "small flute"), in common use since the late eighteenth century, is half the length of a standard flute and plays an octave higher than written. The alto flute is noticeably larger than the standard flute, and its range is a perfect fourth lower. It is a transposing instrument which plays a perfect fourth lower than written.

9. Both have Boehm-system keywork (in fact, the modern alto flute was developed by Boehm), and the fact that they are transposing instruments means that a flautist doesn't need to learn a new set of fingerings for each instrument. Bass flute, a twentieth-century invention, is still quite rare.

A History and Geography of the Flute

10. The holes in early transverse flutes were spaced to give mean tone tuning. This tuning system was popular in Europe from the sixteenth through eighteenth centuries, but it made it difficult for one instrument to play well in more than one key. This limited the flute's usefulness to orchestra.

11. The recorder, a wooden, end-blown, whistle-mouthpiece type flute was very popular in early Western music. It was particularly popular in the Renaissance and Baroque periods. But it is not an ideal orchestral instrument because of its quiet sound. Meanwhile, the keywork on transverse flutes was gradually being improved, and equal temperament, which allows an instrument to play equally well in all keys, became the accepted tuning standard. At that point, the transverse flute, with its wider range of timbre, pitch, and dynamics, became more popular than the recorder. Eventually the flute replaced the recorder so completely that the recorder nearly died out, until an interest in early music and early instruments helped spark a revival in the twentieth century.

12. The fife is a small transverse flute that — like the piccolo — sounds an octave higher than the orchestral flute. Its history since the middle ages is one of military rather than concert use, however. There were at one time fife "calls" used as signals (similar to the bugle calls still in use), and fife and drum corps still play military music.

13. The flute family is also the most widespread aerophone family, with representatives in more Non-Western music traditions around the world than any other non-percussion instrument. Bamboo flutes are common throughout Asia. Panpipes, which have many different-sized tubes bound together rather than finger holes in a single tube, are particularly popular in South America. Many variations of the side-blown and end-blown flutes (including double and triple flutes) have been developed in many cultures. Vessel flutes have been made in many different shapes, including animals and people, out of many different materials, including bone, wood, fruit shells, and pottery. Whistles are usually used for signals rather than music, but bird whistles, which are filled with water to get a bubbling whistle that sounds very much like the trill of a bird, are sometimes found in the percussion section of orchestras and bands. Nose flutes, played with the nose rather than the mouth, are popular in some South Pacific and Indian Ocean countries.

TIP of the DAY

Section headings in informational texts can help you locate information and understand how an author has presented information.

EXERCISES

1. Which detail from the text best explains that flutes are one of the most widely-played instruments?

   A. "The flute family is a large family of instruments…"
   B. "Although many particular kinds of flutes are not widely known…"
   C. "…probably the most common non-percussion instrument found in music traditions around the world."
   D. "There are many different types of flutes played around the world."

   CCSS.ELA-LITERACY.RI.7.1

2. Which paragraph explains how an instrument can be classified as a flute?

   A. paragraph 1
   B. paragraph 2
   C. paragraph 3
   D. paragraph 4

   CCSS.ELA-LITERACY.RI.7.5

3. What is paragraph 5's function in the passage?

   A. It states details about one type of flute.
   B. It provides a transition into the sections on types of flutes.
   C. It explains steps for playing the flute.
   D. It expresses the overall main idea in the passage.

   CCSS.ELA-LITERACY.RI.7.5

4. What is the central idea of paragraph 13?

   A. Bamboo flutes are a type of flute used in Asia, and the panpipe is used in South America.
   B. Flutes have been made in the shapes of animals and people.
   C. Flutes are made with many materials, including bone and wood.
   D. Flutes are used not just in western cultures but also in non-western cultures throughout the world.

   CCSS.ELA-LITERACY.RI.7.2

5. Select the detail below that explains what piccolos and alto flutes have in common.

   A. "…in common use since the late eighteenth century."
   B. "…plays an octave higher than written."
   C. "It is a transposing instrument which plays a perfect fourth lower than written."
   D. "…have Boehm-system keywork…"

   CCSS.ELA-LITERACY.RI.7.1

6. What was Theobald Boehm's contribution to flutes?

   A. He created its general design.
   B. He composed the first piece of flute music.
   C. He introduced it to orchestras across Europe.
   D. He taught younger musicians how to play it.

   CCSS.ELA-LITERACY.RI.7.3

The Song of Wandering Aengus *by William Butler Yeats*

I went out to the hazel wood,
Because a fire was in my head,
And cut and peeled a hazel wand,
And hooked a berry to a thread;
And when white moths were on the wing,
And moth-like stars were flickering out,
I dropped the berry in a stream
And caught a little silver trout.

When I had laid it on the floor
I went to blow the fire a-flame,
But something rustled on the floor,
And someone called me by my name:
It had become a glimmering girl
With apple blossom in her hair
Who called me by my name and ran
And faded through the brightening air.

Though I am old with wandering
Through hollow lands and hilly lands,
I will find out where she has gone,
And kiss her lips and take her hands;
And walk among long dappled grass,
And pluck till time and times are done,
The silver apples of the moon,
The golden apples of the sun.

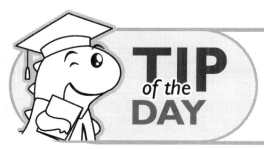

TIP of the DAY

A narrator is the person or thing that tells a story. Poems, though, have speakers rather than narrators.

EXERCISES

1. What does the following line from the first stanza mean?

   Because a fire was in my head,

   A. The speaker had a headache.
   B. The speaker had an idea.
   C. The speaker was confused.
   D. The speaker was happy.

   CCSS.ELA-LITERACY.RL.7.4

2. What impact does the word "glimmering" have in stanza 2?

   A. It emphasizes how beautiful the girl is.
   B. It explains that the room is filled with light.
   C. It states that the girl's hair is dark.
   D. It indicates that the speaker is unsure about seeing the girl.

   CCSS.ELA-LITERACY.RL.7.4

3. What is the central idea of the poem?

   A. The speaker decides to go fishing and catches a fish.
   B. The speaker meets a mysterious girl who appears in his house.
   C. The speaker starts as a young man and then becomes old.
   D. The speaker wants to find a girl he once knew when he was young.

   CCSS.ELA-LITERACY.RL.7.2

4. Which line from the poem best supports your answer to question 4?

   A. "And caught a little silver trout."
   B. "It had become a glimmering girl"
   C. "Though I am old with wandering"
   D. "I will find out where she has gone,"

   CCSS.ELA-LITERACY.RL.7.1

5. Which statement summarizes the final stanza?

   A. The speaker wants to travel to different lands.
   B. The speaker still believes he will find the girl in his old age.
   C. The speaker wants to spend time in nature with the girl.
   D. The speaker is living his last days.

   CCSS.ELA-LITERACY.RL.7.2

6. What tone does the speaker use throughout the poem? Select the best answer.

   A. depressing
   B. hopeful
   C. nervous
   D. enthusiastic

   CCSS.ELA-LITERACY.RL.7.5

WEEK 18

VIDEO EXPLANATIONS

ARGOPREP.COM

WEEK 18 : MONDAY

Restatement/Synonym Clues

CCSS.ELA-LITERACY.L.7.4.A

<u>Key Terms and Examples</u>

Let's review context clues. Context clues are hints that a writer includes to help the reader understand unfamiliar words. There are many types of context clues that help clarify the meaning of words.

What are restatement/synonym clues?

Restatement/synonym clues are context clues that state an informal meaning of the unfamiliar word or include a synonym of the word. There are often signal words such as "or" or "that is" written before the restatement/synonym clue.

The following are examples of restatement/synonym clues.

We were drenched, or <u>completely wet from the rain</u>.

The snowstorm has abated; that is, it has <u>stopped snowing so much</u>.

The castle was under siege — <u>surrounded by the enemy</u>.

The pheasant, <u>a bird</u>, spends most of the time on the ground.

The baby vigorously, <u>or energetically</u>, kicked its legs.

As you use context clues to help you understand what you are reading, you can also use a dictionary to verify if your definition is correct.

EXERCISES

Read each sentence. In the space provided, write the restatement/synonym clue.

1. My dad asked me to take out the rubbish, or garbage.

CCSS.ELA-LITERACY.L.7.4.A

4. Rodrigo's voice was hoarse — dry and raspy — because he was sick.

CCSS.ELA-LITERACY.L.7.4.A

2. It is advantageous to do your homework; that is, it will help you.

CCSS.ELA-LITERACY.L.7.4.A

5. Melissa gingerly, or carefully, walked down the narrow staircase.

CCSS.ELA-LITERACY.L.7.4.A

3. This is a pertinent, or important, law to pass.

CCSS.ELA-LITERACY.L.7.4.A

6. Which answer is accurate, or correct?

CCSS.ELA-LITERACY.L.7.4.A

Cause and Effect Clues

CCSS.ELA-LITERACY.L.7.4.A

Key Terms and Examples

Today we are going to learn about another type of context clue. Remember, context clues are hints that a writer includes to help the reader understand unfamiliar words.

What are cause and effect clues?

Cause and effect clues state a cause and effect pattern. After an unfamiliar word, the effect may be explained in a way that makes it easy to understand the word's meaning.

Cause and effect clues can also work the opposite way. A cause can be explained, while the unfamiliar word is part of the effect. Signal words such as "because," "as a result," "since," "therefore," and "when" often come before cause and effect clues.

The following are examples of cause and effect clues:

I <u>misplaced</u> my science homework; therefore, I got a zero on it.

"Misplaced" means to put in the wrong place. We can figure out the meaning by looking at the effect of misplacing the homework. The effect is that the person got a zero on the homework for misplacing it, so it means that he or she could not find it.

An <u>influx</u> of ants came into our house looking for water since it was hot and dry outside.

"Influx" means that a flow of ants came into the house looking for water. The effect was the influx of ants. We can look at the cause — it was hot and dry outside — to help us understand the meaning of "influx." The ants needed water, so they started coming into the house.

TIP of the DAY

Sometimes context clues appear in a sentence before or after the sentence with the unfamiliar word. Re-read the full paragraph if you do not see context clues in the same sentence as the unfamiliar word.

EXERCISES

Read each sentence. Write the correct meaning of each underlined word.

1. Jenny was <u>reprimanded</u> because she called her sister a mean name.

CCSS.ELA-LITERACY.L.7.4.A

2. There was a thunderstorm, the cake fell off the table, and the wedding dress got dirty; the outdoor wedding was a <u>fiasco</u>.

CCSS.ELA-LITERACY.L.7.4.A

3. Juan broke his ankle, so he had to <u>cease</u> training for the marathon.

CCSS.ELA-LITERACY.L.7.4.A

4. Alexandria was <u>lauded</u> by the teacher when she helped Beatrice after she had been bullied.

CCSS.ELA-LITERACY.L.7.4.A

5. The man and woman <u>reconciled</u> after the woman apologized.

CCSS.ELA-LITERACY.L.7.4.A

6. Marie Curie became a <u>renowned</u> scientist after discovering radioactivity.

CCSS.ELA-LITERACY.L.7.4.A

WEEK 18 : FRIDAY

Analogies

CCSS.ELA-LITERACY.L.7.5.B

Key Terms and Examples

What are analogies?

Analogies are comparisons between two things. Analogies are used to provide explanation or clarify. Analogies are not figures of speech and are not metaphors and similes. Analogies, instead, make logical arguments to explain connections between things that are different.

When you come across an analogy, think about the traits that the two things have in common.

One way to practice analogies is by using the following pattern:

Head *is to* body *as* ice cream *is to* _____ .

The phrase "is to" connects the two things that are being compared. The word "as" means that the second comparison will follow the same pattern as the first comparison.

First, think about the comparison of head and body. A head is at the top of a body. This comparison will help you figure out what word should be placed in the blank spot. Ice cream can be found at the top of what? Ice cream can be found at the top of an ice cream cone.

The full analogy is:

Head *is to* body *as* ice cream *is to* ice cream cone.

Let's look at one more analogy.

Trickle *is to* faucet *as* whimper *is to* _____ .

What does the word "trickle" have in common with the word "faucet"? Water can trickle out of a faucet. We'll use the same pattern to figure out the missing word in the second comparison. A whimper can come out of what? A whimper, a sound someone makes, can come out of a mouth.

The completed analogy is:

Trickle *is to* faucet *as* whimper *is to* mouth.

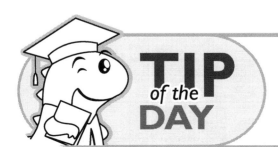

TIP of the DAY

There are four types of analogies: synonym, antonym, descriptive, and part to whole. When you read an analogy, its category can help you figure out the missing word.

164

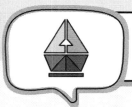

EXERCISES

Read each analogy. Then select the best word that correctly completes the analogy.

1. Scrumptious is to donut as _____ is to spoiled meat.

   A. refrigerated
   B. disgusting
   C. warm
   D. animal

   CCSS.ELA-LITERACY.L.7.5.B

2. Honk is to car as _____ is to dog.

   A. mouth
   B. head
   C. bark
   D. sound

   CCSS.ELA-LITERACY.L.7.5.B

3. South is to north as left is to _____.

   A. right
   B. direction
   C. west
   D. east

   CCSS.ELA-LITERACY.L.7.5.B

4. Pink is to red as cold is to _____.

   A. color
   B. cool
   C. blue
   D. freezing

   CCSS.ELA-LITERACY.L.7.5.B

5. Lion is to cub as bowl is to _____.

   A. kitchen
   B. teaspoon
   C. cat
   D. liquid

   CCSS.ELA-LITERACY.L.7.5.B

6. Remote control is to buttons as bicycle is to _____.

   A. travel
   B. seat
   C. handles
   D. pedals

   CCSS.ELA-LITERACY.L.7.5.B

WEEK 19

VIDEO EXPLANATIONS

ARGOPREP.COM

The Arrow and the Song *by Henry Wadsworth Longfellow*

I shot an arrow into the air,
It fell to earth, I knew not where;
For, so swiftly it flew, the sight
Could not follow it in its flight.

I breathed a song into the air,
It fell to earth, I knew not where;
For who has sight so keen and strong,
That it can follow the flight of song?

Long, long afterward, in an oak
I found the arrow, still unbroke;
And the song, from beginning to end,
I found again in the heart of a friend.

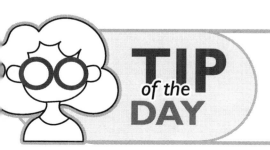

TIP of the DAY

Many poems have quatrains, which are stanzas with four lines. Can you figure out what the Latin root «quat» means? If you said «four,» you are correct!

167

EXERCISES

1. What type of poem is "The Arrow and the Song"?

   A. lyric poem
   B. acrostic
   C. haiku
   D. epic poem

   CCSS.ELA-LITERACY.RL.7.5

2. How does the poetry structure impact the meaning of the poem?

   A. The acrostic structure helps visualize the author's message.
   B. The haiku structure simplifies the author's thoughts in a clear way.
   C. The epic structure allows the author to tell a long narrative.
   D. The lyric structure is musical and expresses the author's feelings.

   CCSS.ELA-LITERACY.RL.7.5

3. What do the first and second stanza have in common?

   A. In both stanzas, the arrow and song travel far away, and the speaker leaves on a journey to find them.
   B. In both stanzas, the arrow and song affect only the speaker of the poem.
   C. In both stanzas, the arrow and song are sent into the world, and the speaker is not sure how far they travel.
   D. In both stanzas, the arrow and song are found by someone in the speaker's family.

   CCSS.ELA-LITERACY.RL.7.2

4. How does the line repetition in stanzas 1 and 2 impact the poem?

   A. The repetition explains a character trait of the speaker.
   B. The repetition summarizes both stanzas
   C. The repetition foreshadows the events of the third stanza.
   D. The repetition stresses the central ideas of the stanzas.

   CCSS.ELA-LITERACY.RL.7.4

5. What could the arrow and the song represent?

   A. The arrow represents strength, and the song represents weakness.
   B. The arrow represents unkind words, and the song represents kind words.
   C. The arrow and the song represent long-lost love.
   D. The arrow and the song represent the passing of time.

   CCSS.ELA-LITERACY.RL.7.2

6. What is the theme of the poem?

   A. We need to remain strong rather than weak throughout life.
   B. We need to use words wisely because we do not know how they could harm or help someone.
   C. Sometimes we still love someone from the past.
   D. Time passes quickly just as an arrow or song can travel quickly.

   CCSS.ELA-LITERACY.RL.7.2

Classifying Musical Instruments *by Catherine Schmidt-Jones*

Introduction

1. There are two common ways to classify musical instruments. One way is to group them as they are in a Western orchestra: strings, woodwinds, brass, and percussion. This method is more widely recognized, particularly among non-musicians, and it is very useful in its traditional setting, Western classical and art music. However, it is difficult or confusing to apply to the many non-orchestral instruments.

2. The other way, first published in 1914 by Erich von Hornbostel and Curt Sachs, is to group instruments according to how their sounds are produced. This method can be used to classify any instrument and is now preferred by most musicologists. The Hornbostel-Sachs method is more specific, more inclusive, and more accurate:

    -   More specific - Categories are subdivided into smaller and smaller categories, making a sort of family tree of related instruments (related by function, not by history).

    -   More inclusive - Any instrument can be categorized.

    -   More accurate - Instruments are grouped according to how sounds are produced, not according to which instruments the composer is likely to group them with in the music or which orchestra member is likely to play them.

Chordophones

3. In a chordophone, the sound is made by vibrating strings. The main groups of chordophones are classified according to the relationship between the strings and the resonator. (Resonators pick up the original vibrations and vibrate sympathetically with them, amplifying the original sounds and altering them so that they sound more musical.) Subcategories depend on how the string is played (plucked or bowed for example), and types of resonators. A banjo is classified as a plucked lute chordophone. Harps are one of the main subcategories of chordophone.

Chordophone Categories

4. -   In zithers, the strings are stretched across, over, or inside a resonator, or between two resonators. The resonator can be a hollow tube, a gourd, a board, a hollow box, or even a pit in the ground. Some have fingerboards with or without frets; some have a keyboard with a complex mechanism; many are simply a multitude of strings strung from one end of the resonator to the other. The strings can be struck (as in a piano or hammered dulcimer) or plucked (harpsichord or Appalachian dulcimer).

5. • In lutes, the strings stretch across the resonator and up a neck. They may be plucked (guitar, banjo) or bowed (violin, fiddle).

6. • In lyres, the strings leave the resonator at right angles to an edge and run to a cross bar that is held away from the resonator(as in the classical Greek lyre that is so often used as a symbol of music).

7. • In harps (like the orchestral harp and the Irish harp), the strings leave the resonator at a slant (smaller than a right angle) up to a neck connected to the resonator.

8. • In a musical bow, the string or strings are stretched from one end of a wooden bow to the other. Some have resonators, but many don't. They can be plucked or bowed.

Aerophones

9. In aerophones, the sound is produced by vibrating air (usually inside the instrument). The instrument, or parts of the instrument, are shaped (often into a tube or set of tubes) so that the vibrations will be a particular length, and so a particular pitch. Aerophones are grouped according to what causes the air to begin vibrating. The melodeon, like its close relatives the accordion and concertina, is a free-reed aerophone.

Aerophone Categories

10. • In whistles, the air is blown at a sharp edge in the instrument (as in recorders as well as police whistles).

11. • In blowhole instruments, the air is blown across the sharp edge at the blowhole. When the instrument is tube-shaped, the blowhole can be in the end ("end-blown", as in panpipes), or in the side of the instrument ("side-blown", as in a fife).

12. • In reed instruments, the vibration of a reed or reeds begins the air vibration. In single reed (saxophone, for example) and double reed (oboe) instruments, the one or two reeds are part of the mouthpiece. In bagpipes and in free-reed instruments (such as harmonica and accordion), the single or double reeds are mounted somewhere inside the instrument and there can be many of them - sometimes a different reed for every pitch.

13. • In cup mouthpiece instruments, the player buzzes the lips against the mouthpiece, causing a sympathetic vibration in the air inside the instrument (bugle, conch shell).

14. • The pipes of an organ have a sharp edge like a whistle, but the pipes are filled with air from something other than a mouth or nose, usually a bellows of some sort.

15. • Free aerophones (bull-roarers, toy spinning tops), cause vibrations in the air around them rather than inside them.

Membranophones

16. In membranophones, the sound begins with the vibration of a stretched membrane, or skin (often an actual animal skin), but the skin is usually stretched across a resonator. Membranophones are usually classified according to the shape of the resonating body of the instrument.

17. Membranophones are classified by their basic shape. For example, a drum that is wider at the top and bottom than in the middle is a waisted tubular drum.

Membranophone Categories

18. • Tubular drums are divided into cylindrical, conical, barrel, long-waisted (hourglass-shaped), goblet (with a stem at the base), and footed (with feet around the edge of the bottom).

19. • Kettledrums or vessel drums have rounded bottoms.

20. • In frame drums, the membrane is stretched over a frame, usually making a wide, shallow instrument. (Tambourines are in this category.)

21. • Friction drums come in a variety of shapes. Instead of beating on the membrane, the player runs a stick through a hole in the membrane.

22. • In mirlitons, the membrane is made to vibrate by blowing air across it. These are the only membranophones that are not drums. (Kazoos are in this category.)

Idiophones

23. In idiophones, it is the vibration of the instrument itself that is the main source of the musical sound. Idiophones are classified according to what you do to them to make them vibrate.

24. Bells and steel drums are percussion idiophones; Steel drums are hit with sticks held by the player; a bell is hit by the clapper inside the bell.

Idiophone Categories

25. • Percussion idiophones are hit with sticks, beaters, or clappers (bells, steel drums).

26. • Shaken idiophones are shaken (maracas, eggs, jingle bells).

27. • Concussion idiophones are played by clashing two of them together (castanets, claves, spoons).

28. • Friction idiophones are made to vibrate by rubbing them (as when you make a wine glass ring by rubbing its rim).

29. • Scraped idiophones are played by scraping a stick across a set of notches or corrugations on the instrument (guiro, washboard).

30. • Stamping idiophones are stamped on the ground, floor, or hard surface. (Tap shoes are in this category.)

31. • If the main sound is coming from the surface that is being stamped on, it is a stamped idiophone.

32. • Plucked idiophones have a thin tongue of metal or bamboo that vibrates when plucked (jew's harp, mbira or thumb piano).

Electrophones

33. An instrument that is not amplified electrically is an acoustic instrument. There are instruments (such as the electric-acoustic guitar, vibraphone, and electric saxophone) that keep their acoustic resonators but are also amplified and altered electronically. Actually any instrument sound that has been through a microphone and amplifier, or even been saved as a recording, belongs in this category. These instruments are probably best categorized as they would be before being amplified.

TIP of the DAY

Informational texts include an overarching central idea or thesis statement in the introduction. Pay close attention to the introduction to have a better understanding of what the author is trying prove in the text.

EXERCISES

1. Which text structure does the author use in the passage?

    A. cause and effect
    B. problem and solution
    C. description
    D. sequential order

    CCSS.ELA-LITERACY.RI.7.5

3. Which method do musicologists prefer today?

    A. grouping instruments according to the materials used to build them
    B. grouping instruments according to how their sounds are produced
    C. grouping instruments according to their geographic location
    D. grouping instruments according to the genre of music they play

    CCSS.ELA-LITERACY.RI.7.1

2. How do the category sections impact the passage?

    A. The category sections summarize the steps for playing each type of instrument.
    B. The category sections act as transitional sections.
    C. The category sections state the central idea of the passage.
    D. The category sections give examples of what is being explained in the current section.

    CCSS.ELA-LITERACY.RI.7.5

4. Based on the passage, what does the root "aero" mean in the word "aerophone"?

    A. musical
    B. air
    C. play
    D. key

    CCSS.ELA-LITERACY.RI.7.4

EXERCISES

5. What is the most important difference between membranophones and idiophones?

   A. Idiophones are hit with sticks, beaters, or clappers, while membranophones have rounded bottoms.
   B. Membranophones are hit with sticks, beaters, or clappers, while idiophones have rounded bottoms.
   C. Idiophones have sound that is made by the vibration of a stretched skin, while the vibration of the membranophone instrument itself is the main source of the musical sound.
   D. Membranophones have sound that is made by the vibration of a stretched skin, while the vibration of the idiophone instrument itself is the main source of the musical sound.

   CCSS.ELA-LITERACY.RI.7.2

6. What is the purpose of paragraph 33?

   A. It explains how electrophones compare with idiophones.
   B. It explains how electrophones contrast with membranophones and idiophones.
   C. It explains how electrophones compare with chordophones and aerophones.
   D. It explains how electrophones contrast with all other categories.

   CCSS.ELA-LITERACY.RI.7.5

NOTES

Adapted from The Call of the Wild *by Jack London*

The Call of the Wild is about a dog named Buck who is stolen from his owner and forced to be a sled dog in the Yukon Territory.

1. For two days and nights this express car was dragged along at the tail of shrieking locomotives; and for two days and nights Buck neither ate nor drank. In his anger he had met the first advances of the express messengers with growls, and they had retaliated by teasing him. When he flung himself against the bars, quivering and frothing, they laughed at him and taunted him. They growled and barked like detestable dogs, mewed, and flapped their arms and crowed. It was all very silly, he knew; but therefore the more outrage to his dignity, and his anger waxed and waxed. He did not mind the hunger so much, but the lack of water caused him severe suffering and fanned his wrath to fever-pitch. For that matter, high-strung and finely sensitive, the ill treatment had flung him into a fever, which was fed by the inflammation of his parched and swollen throat and tongue.

2. He was glad for one thing: the rope was off his neck. That had given them an unfair advantage; but now that it was off, he would show them. They would never get another rope around his neck. Upon that he was resolved. For two days and nights he neither ate nor drank, and during those two days and nights of torment, he accumulated a fund of wrath that boded ill for whoever first fell foul of him. His eyes turned blood-shot, and he was metamorphosed into a raging fiend. So changed was he that his old owner himself would not have recognized him; and the express messengers breathed with relief when they bundled him off the train at Seattle.

3. Four men gingerly carried the crate from the wagon into a small, high-walled backyard. A stout man, with a red sweater that sagged generously at the neck, came out and signed the book for the driver. That was the man, Buck divined, the next tormentor, and he hurled himself savagely against the bars. The man smiled grimly, and brought a hatchet and a club.

4. "You ain't going to take him out now?" the driver asked.

5. "Sure," the man replied, driving the hatchet into the crate for a pry.

6. There was an instantaneous scattering of the four men who had carried it in, and from safe perches on top the wall they prepared to watch the performance.

7. Buck rushed at the splintering wood, sinking his teeth into it, surging and wrestling with it. Wherever the hatchet fell on the outside, he was there on the inside, snarling and growling, as furiously anxious to get out as the man in the red sweater was calmly intent on getting him out.

8. "Now, you red-eyed devil," he said, when he had made an opening sufficient for the passage of Buck's body. At the same time he dropped the hatchet and shifted the club to his right hand.

9. And Buck was truly a red-eyed devil, as he drew himself together for the spring, hair bristling, mouth foaming, a mad glitter in his blood-shot eyes. Straight at the man he launched his one hundred and forty pounds of fury, surcharged with the pent passion of two days and nights. In mid air, just as his jaws were about to close on the man, he received a shock that checked his body and brought his teeth together with an agonizing clip. He whirled over, fetching the ground on his back and side.

175

He had never been struck by a club in his life, and did not understand. With a snarl that was part bark and more scream he was again on his feet and launched into the air. And again the shock came and he was brought crushingly to the ground. This time he was aware that it was the club, but his madness knew no caution. A dozen times he charged, and as often the club broke the charge and smashed him down.

10. After a particularly fierce blow, he crawled to his feet, too dazed to rush. He staggered limply about, the blood flowing from his nose and mouth and ears, his beautiful coat sprayed and flecked with bloody slaver. Then the man advanced and deliberately dealt him a frightful blow on the nose. All the pain he had endured was as nothing compared with the exquisite agony of this. With a roar that was almost lionlike in its ferocity, he again hurled himself at the man. But the man, shifting the club from right to left, coolly caught him by the under jaw, at the same time wrenching downward and backward. Buck described a complete circle in the air, and half of another, then crashed to the ground on his head and chest.

11. For the last time he rushed. The man struck the shrewd blow he had purposely withheld for so long, and Buck crumpled up and went down, knocked utterly senseless.

12. "He's no slouch at dog-breakin', that's what I say," one of the men on the wall cried enthusiastically.

13. "Druther break cayuses any day, and twice on Sundays," was the reply of the driver, as he climbed on the wagon and started the horses.

14. Buck's senses came back to him, but not his strength. He lay where he had fallen, and from there he watched the man in the red sweater.

15. "'Answers to the name of Buck,'" the man soliloquized, quoting from the saloon-keeper's letter which had announced the consignment of the crate and contents. "Well, Buck, my boy," he went on in a genial voice, "you've learned your place, and I know mine. Be a good dog and all will go well. Be a bad dog, and I'll whale the stuffin' out of you. Understand?"

16. As he spoke he fearlessly patted the head he had so mercilessly pounded, and though Buck's hair involuntarily bristled at the touch of the hand, he endured it without protest.

17. When the man brought him water he drank eagerly, and later bolted a generous meal of raw meat, chunk by chunk, from the man's hand.

18. He was beaten (he knew that); but he was not broken. He saw, once for all, that he stood no chance against a man with a club. He had learned the lesson, and in all his afterlife he never forgot it. That club was a revelation. It was his introduction to the reign of primitive law, and he met the introduction halfway. As the days went by, other dogs came, in crates and at the ends of ropes, some docilely, and some raging and roaring as he had come; and, one and all, he watched them pass under the dominion of the man in the red sweater.

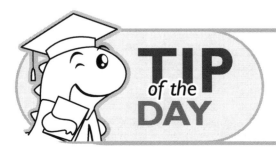

TIP of the DAY

Narratives follow a plot line that starts with introducing a main conflict. Throughout the story, the problem worsens. Ask yourself how the conflict is building as you read a narrative.

EXERCISES

1. Identify two main ideas in paragraph 1.

_____

_____

_____

_____

CCSS.ELA-LITERACY.RL.7.2

2. What type of literary device is used in paragraph 1? Support your answer with two details from the text.

_____

_____

_____

_____

CCSS.ELA-LITERACY.RL.7.4

3. In paragraph 2, why did "the express messengers [breathe] with relief when they bundled him off the train at Seattle"? Select the best answer.

  A. They felt upset about Buck's treatment.
  B. Buck turned vicious and angry.
  C. Buck refused to eat food or drink water.
  D. The men wanted to give Buck back to his owner.

CCSS.ELA-LITERACY.RL.7.3

4. Select the detail from the text that supports your answer from question 3.

  A. "...the rope was off his neck."
  B. "That had given them an unfair advantage..."
  C. "For two days and nights he neither ate nor drank..."
  D. "...he was metamorphosed into a raging fiend."

CCSS.ELA-LITERACY.RL.7.1

5. How does paragraph 9 impact the story?

  A. Buck takes revenge on the men who abused him.
  B. The men are frightened of Buck when he attacks them.
  C. The men want to give Buck away to someone else.
  D. Buck is clubbed for the first time, which changes him.

CCSS.ELA-LITERACY.RL.7.2

6. What is Buck's perspective in paragraph 18?

  A. Buck realizes that he cannot win against a man with a club.
  B. Buck feels that the new dogs are weaker than he is.
  C. Buck wants to help the new dogs who are attacked by the men.
  D. Buck tries to understand the man in the red sweater.

CCSS.ELA-LITERACY.RL.7.6

WEEK 20

VIDEO EXPLANATIONS

ARGOPREP.COM

Home Sweet Home

WEEK 20 : MONDAY

Connotation and Denotation Practice 1

CCSS.ELA-LITERACY.L.7.5.C

Key Terms

What does denotation mean?

Denotation is the dictionary definition of a word. All words have a literal meaning that we can find in the dictionary.

What does connotation mean?

Words have synonyms with similar denotations, but a word's synonyms have slightly different shades of meaning. Connotation is the emotion related to the word or the cultural meaning. Connotation helps express a point of view, which can be positive, neutral, or negative.

Examples

Let's look at the following pairs of words.

curious

nosy

The denotation of both "curious" and "nosy" describes someone who wants to know more about something. These two words have different connotations, though.

The connotation of "curious" is positive. It means that someone is eager to learn.

The connotation of "nosy" is negative. It means that someone is interfering when they shouldn't.

Let's take a look at another pair of words.

residence

home

The denotation of both "residence" and "home" is a place where someone lives. Their connotations express different emotional meanings, though.

The connotation of "residence" is neutral. It is similar to the denotation.

The connotation of "home" is positive, though. It expresses feelings of safety, happiness, and coziness.

TIP of the DAY

Words can have different connotations in different cultures. Do you know someone from a different part of the country or world? He or she may view a word's meaning differently than you do.

EXERCISES

Read each pair of words. In the space provided, write "positive" next to the word if it has a positive connotation. Write "neutral" next to the word if it has a neutral connotation. Write "negative" next to the word if it has a negative connotation.

1. unique _____

   strange _____

   CCSS.ELA-LITERACY.L.7.5.C

2. spit _____

   saliva _____

   CCSS.ELA-LITERACY.L.7.5.C

3. youthful _____

   immature _____

   CCSS.ELA-LITERACY.L.7.5.C

4. confident _____

   pushy _____

   CCSS.ELA-LITERACY.L.7.5.C

5. cheap _____

   inexpensive _____

   CCSS.ELA-LITERACY.L.7.5.C

6. slender _____

   scrawny _____

   CCSS.ELA-LITERACY.L.7.5.C

Connotation and Denotation Practice 2

CCSS.ELA-LITERACY.L.7.5.C

Key Terms and Examples

Let's review denotation and connotation. Denotation is the dictionary definition of a word. Connotation helps express an emotion or cultural meaning. Connotation can be positive, neutral, or negative.

If you read the following word, what is its denotation?

relaxed

Relaxed means to be free from anxiety or tension.

What are similar words with different connotations?

laid-back (positive)

lazy (negative)

These words have similar denotations but express different connotations.

Some words have more than one denotation, or dictionary definition. The multiple definitions can each have their own connotations.

EXERCISES

For each word listed below, write a similar word that has either a positive connotation or a negative connotation.

1. smell _____

CCSS.ELA-LITERACY.L.7.5.C

2. conversational _____

CCSS.ELA-LITERACY.L.7.5.C

3. crowded _____

CCSS.ELA-LITERACY.L.7.5.C

4. short _____

CCSS.ELA-LITERACY.L.7.5.C

5. tall _____

CCSS.ELA-LITERACY.L.7.5.C

6. economical _____

CCSS.ELA-LITERACY.L.7.5.C

Connotation and Denotation Practice 3

CCSS.ELA-LITERACY.L.7.5.C

Key Terms

Remember, denotation is the dictionary definition of a word. Connotation is the emotional response to a word. Connotations can be positive, neutral, or negative.

If we read a list of synonyms that have similar denotations, how do their connotations differ? The synonyms will have different shades of meaning, ranging from least positive (or neutral) to most positive; or least negative (or neutral) to most negative.

Examples

Let's look at a series of synonyms with similar denotations.

pleasant, okay, nice, delightful, charming

How do their connotations differ? If we order these words from neutral to most positive, here is how they would be listed:

okay

pleasant

nice

charming

delightful

Let's look at another list of synonyms. How do their connotations differ?

mean, unfriendly, rude, nasty, evil

If we order these words from least to most negative, here is how they would be listed:

unfriendly

rude

mean

nasty

evil

TIP of the DAY

In your own writing, think about how to clearly express your ideas. Use a thesaurus if you need help brainstorming synonyms. Then choose the synonym that most clearly communicates your idea.

183

EXERCISES

Read each group of words. In the space provided, list the words in order from least positive to most positive or least negative to most negative.

1. exquisite, attractive, pretty, fair, beautiful

CCSS.ELA-LITERACY.L.7.5.C

4. furious, annoyed, aggravated, mad, enraged

CCSS.ELA-LITERACY.L.7.5.C

2. spoiled, putrid, rotten, bad, overripe

CCSS.ELA-LITERACY.L.7.5.C

5. crisp, cold, cool, arctic, frigid

CCSS.ELA-LITERACY.L.7.5.C

3. glum, unhappy, heartbroken, depressed, sad

CCSS.ELA-LITERACY.L.7.5.C

6. joyful, delighted, happy, ecstatic, euphoric

CCSS.ELA-LITERACY.L.7.5.C

ANSWER KEY

ARGOPREP.COM

VIDEO EXPLANATIONS ▶

ANSWER KEY

WEEK 1

Monday
1. C   2. B   3. A   4. D   5. B   6. C

Wednesday
1. B   2. C   3. D   4. B   5. C   6. A

Friday
1. Answers may vary. An example of a possible response:
   In the first stanza, the author is describing what happens when the sun rises. For example, the poem states that the sun starts to rise slowly, "A ribbon at a time." The poem then describes how the church steeples "swam in amethyst." The reader can picture the color of the sunrise covering the sky and buildings.
2. Answers may vary. An example of a possible response:
   The rhythm of the poem begins to change in stanza 3. While the first half of the poem describes the sun rising, the second half of the poem describes the sun setting. For example, the poem states, "But how he set, I know not." The following line, "There seemed a purple stile" describes the color of the sunset.
3. D   4. C   5. B   6. C

WEEK 2

Monday
1. D   3. A   5. During the movie
2. C   4. singing pop songs   6. Hannah and Danny

Wednesday
1. independent   4. While we waited   6. we could not buy the new video
2. dependent   5. Bryce would rather eat lima   game
3. because he threw his food   beans

Friday
1. A   2. B   3. A
4. Answers may vary. A possible answer:
   While we were standing in line for movie tickets, lightning flashed.
5. Answers may vary. A possible answer:
   The girl with curly brown hair danced on the stage.
6. Answers may vary. A possible answer:
   The man in a pinstriped suit walked the dog.

WEEK 3

Monday
1. C   2. C   3. D   4. B   5. A   6. B

Wednesday

1. D   2. B   3. C   4. A   5. C   6. D

Friday

1. Answers may vary. An example of a possible response:

   The mood of the poem is quiet and peaceful. For example, the narrator states, "To watch his woods fill up with snow." The narrator is stopping to think and look at the nature around him. The narrator also states, "To stop without a farmhouse near." The narrator and his horse are alone in the woods, and there is silence around them.

2. Answers may vary. An example of a possible response:

   The poem's main conflict is that the narrator would like to stay in the woods, in the silence, but knows that he must continue on to reach his destination and obligations. For example, the poem states, "He gives his harness bells a shake/ To ask if there is some mistake." The horse is urging the narrator not to stay in the woods. The poem also states, "The woods are lovely, dark and deep,/ But I have promises to keep." The narrator admits that he cannot stay and must move on with his journey.

3. A   4. D   5. A   6. B

WEEK 4

Monday

1. The monkey was hungry; the zookeeper gave him a banana.
2. The marathon began; hundreds of people started running.
3. Becca loves to read, and her favorite books are the *Harry Potter* series.
4. The soccer team lost two games, so they practiced harder.
5. He gave the dog a treat, for the dog performed a trick.
6. Craig wanted to watch a movie, but he had to finish his chores.

Wednesday

1. B
2. C
3. A
4. Since the dancer broke his ankle
5. Before you leave
6. although she prefers strawberries

Friday

1. C   2. D   3. B   4. A   5. A   6. D

WEEK 5

Monday

1. D   2. B   3. B   4. C   5. A   6. C

Wednesday

1. D   2. C   3. B   4. D   5. D   6. A

Friday

1. Answers will vary. An example of a possible response:

   The tubas that are more useful in bands are E flat and B flat. The text states, "E flat and B flat are more useful in bands..." The text also states that "F and C are more common in orchestras."

2. Answers will vary. An example of a possible response:
   Smaller brass instruments only need three valves to get notes in tune. The text states, "For most of the smaller brass instruments (trumpets, horns, and so on), three valves is enough to get all the notes reasonably in tune." Tubas, though, are so large that they need extra valves to play high and low notes in tune. Additionally, the text states that, "They also make it possible to get more notes in the lowest octave of the instrument."

3. D   4. A   5. B   6. C

WEEK 6

Monday
1. D
2. C
3. A

4. The little girl said, "My name is Laura."
5. Have you ever visited the Atlantic Ocean?
6. John and I sit next to each other in class.

Wednesday
1. During the movie, we ate popcorn and candy.
2. Yes, there was a supercontinent called Pangea.
3. To make a cake, we need flour and eggs.

4. Because she was allergic, she had to stay away from the dog.
5. When Claire hit the ball, she ran to first base.
6. If you like chocolate, you'll love this pie.

Friday
1. cumulative adjectives
2. coordinate adjectives
3. coordinate adjectives
4. B
5. A
6. C

WEEK 7

Monday
1. D   2. B   3. B   4. C   5. D   6. A

Wednesday
1. C   2. C   3. D   4. D   5. A   6. D

Friday
1. Answers may vary. An example of a possible response:
   The visitor foremost is mysterious. For example, the text states, "...she noticed that he wore big blue spectacles with sidelights, and had a bushy side-whisker over his coat-collar that completely hid his cheeks and face." The visitor hides his face completely throughout the story. Another example is when Mrs. Hall finds him, "still standing there, like a man of stone, his back hunched, his collar turned up, his dripping hat-brim turned down, hiding his face and ears completely."
2. Answers may vary. An example of a possible response:
   The description, "He staggered into the Coach and Horses, more dead than alive as it seemed..." means that the visitor seems exhausted or ill. The word "staggered" means that he had difficulty walking. The phrase "more dead than alive" means that the visitor had very little energy.
3. B   4. B   5. A   6. D

ANSWER KEY

WEEK 8

Monday
1. Early populations settled in an area because of agriculture.
2. What happens to an economy during a famine?
3. Windmills and watermills are examples of technology created during the Middle Ages.
4. Medieval China had a structured government and advanced political system.
5. Part of Africa is covered by the Sahara Desert, and its boundary can be seen on a map.
6. We are studying the cultural contributions of Medieval Japan.

Wednesday
1. To prove our hypothesis, we are going to observe what happens during the experiment.
2. Pollution is harming the environment.
3. We began an inquiry to find out if music helps plants grow.
4. The evidence showed us that a chemical reaction had taken place.
5. The atmosphere is mostly made up of nitrogen.
6. A characteristic of a frog is its smooth, slimy skin.

Friday
1. We calculated the perimeter of the rectangle.
2. Figure out the variable in the equation.
3. When you split a circle in half, each side has symmetry.
4. Show the minimum and maximum on the number line.
5. Estimate the probability that Jennifer will choose a green card.
6. Round the number to the nearest decimal.

WEEK 9

Monday

| 1. C | 2. D | 3. A | 4. B | 5. B | 6. D |

Wednesday

| 1. C | 2. D | 3. C | 4. B | 5. A | 6. A |

Friday
1. Answers will vary. An example of a possible response:
   Aztec ruler Moctezuma Illhuicamina had his face carved into the rock at the bottom of Chapultepec Hill. The text also states that he ordered "the construction of the Tlaxpana aqueduct." Another Aztec leader also modified the hill. Moctezuma Xocoyotzin wanted pools for raising exotic fish storing water. According to the text, he also ordered that "plants and trees from across the empire be planted in the Chapultepec forest."
2. Answers will vary. An example of a possible response:

New Spain was ruled by Viceroy Bernardo de Gálvez, and under his rule, a country house at the top of Chapultepec Hill began being built. Bernardo de Gálvez died before it was completed, possibly due to being poisoned. Some people thought that he was not building a country house, but was actually building a military fortress for revolting against the Spanish. Due to this rumor, the Crown stopped construction on the building.

3. C   4. D   5. D   6. B

WEEK 10

Monday

1. B   2. C   3. C

4. Answers may vary. An example of a possible response: Jasmine hurled the ball.

5. Answers may vary. An example of a possible response: The soup tasted superb.

6. Answers may vary. An example of a possible response: The caterpillar inched leisurely across the leaf.

Wednesday

1. Answers may vary. An example of a possible response: My mom wants us to change our behavior.

2. Answers may vary. An example of a possible response: The cookie jar was empty.

3. Answers may vary. An example of a possible response: Kim will win first place because she is the best dancer.

4. Answers may vary. An example of a possible response: Mrs. Tuttle was upset with the noisy class.

5. Answers may vary. An example of a possible response: Even though the judges disliked his dish, the chef stayed positive.

6. Answers may vary. An example of a possible response: The sunset looks gorgeous, so we should stay at the beach.

Friday

1. Answers may vary. An example of a possible response: The towering man had to duck under the door.

2. Answers may vary. An example of a possible response: We joined in a circle.

3. Answers may vary. An example of a possible response: The three girls form a singing group.

4. C   5. A   6. B

WEEK 11

Monday

1. D   2. C   3. D   4. C   5. A   6. B

Wednesday

1. B   2. B   3. C   4. D   5. C   6. A

Friday
1. Answers will vary. An example of a possible response:
   In the poem, the word "diverged" means divided. For example, the poem states that there were two roads that diverged. This means that they divided into two directions. The narrator also "looked down one..." He looked down one of the roads that had split off from the other.
2. Answers will vary. An example of a possible response:
   The poem's setting takes place in the woods during fall. For example, the text states that the narrator is in a "yellow wood." This indicates that the narrator is in the woods and that the leaves have turned yellow. Since the leaves are yellow, the time of year must be fall. The narrator also sees leaves on the paths, as the text states in the third stanza. "In leaves no step had trodden black..." helps explain that the narrator is in the woods.

3. A   4. D   5. D   6. B

WEEK 12

Monday
1. medicine for counteracting the effects of poison
2. completely clear and transparent
3. outgoing and sociable
4. a crack forming an opening
5. a sample of a substance or material
6. intelligence and quickness of learning

Wednesday
1. precious stone
2. historical time period
3. liquid or frozen water that falls from the earth's atmosphere
4. B
5. D
6. C

Friday
1. variety or group of many
2. serious and sad
3. took their time
4. D
5. B
6. A

WEEK 13

Monday
1. D   2. D   3. A   4. C   5. B   6. D

Wednesday
1. D   2. B   3. D   4. D   5. A   6. C

Friday
1. Answers may vary. An example of a possible response:
    The boarders have worked on ships and have been out to sea for a long time. For example, the passage states, "They were nearly all whalemen..." This explains the men's occupation at sea. The text also states, "They were a tan and brawny company, with overgrown beards; an unshorn, shaggy set..." These details explain that they have been on ships for a long time because they have not had a chance to shave their beards or update their clothes.
2. Answers may vary. An example of a possible response:
    An example of figurative language in paragraph 2 is the simile, "This young fellow's healthy cheek is like a sun-toasted pear in hue." The simile is used to describe the color of the young man's skin, which looks tan and perhaps red.
3. C   4. D   5. C   6. D

WEEK 14

Monday
1. A   2. B   3. C   4. C   5. D   6. B

Wednesday
1. B   2. D   3. A   4. C   5. C   6. A

Friday
1. C   2. B   3. A   4. B   5. A   6. D

WEEK 15

Monday
1. B   2. C   3. A   4. C   5. B   6. D

Wednesday
1. A   2. D   3. B   4. B   5. D   6. B

Friday
1. Answers may vary. An example of a possible response:
    Ragtime is often played on the piano and is a mixture of influences from Africa and Europe. For example, the European influence in ragtime is "its repeated stanzas and trio sections." The African influence can be heard in "the syncopated rhythms which make ragtime so easily recognizable."
2. Answers may vary. An example of a possible response:
    The author's point of view in paragraph 2 is that racism must have had an influence on Joplin's life and career since he was a black man. He was limited on where he could play as a musician, and that made his path to success far more difficult.
3. A   4. B   5. C   6. B

ANSWER KEY

WEEK 16

Monday
1. Achilles' heel
2. Scrooge
3. Uncle Sam
4. Pandora's box
5. Goliath
6. Casanova

Wednesday
1. he could eat an entire Thanksgiving turkey
2. weighed a ton
3. an eternity
4. I died from embarrassment
5. she reaches the clouds
6. There are a million reasons

Friday
1. C 2. A 3. B 4. B 5. B 6. D

WEEK 17

Monday
1. D 2. A 3. C 4. B 5. C 6. C

Wednesday
1. C 2. C 3. B 4. D 5. D 6. A

Friday
1. B 2. A 3. D 4. D 5. B 6. B

WEEK 18

Monday
1. garbage
2. it will help you
3. important
4. dry and raspy
5. carefully
6. correct

Wednesday
Answers may vary slightly.
1. scolded
2. disaster
3. stop
4. praised
5. reunited
6. famous

Friday
1. B 2. C 3. A 4. D 5. B 6. D

WEEK 19

Monday
1. A 2. D 3. C 4. D 5. B 6. B

Wednesday
1. C 2. D 3. B 4. B 5. D 6. D

ANSWER KEY

Friday

1. Answers may vary. An example of a possible response:
   Buck is starving, dehydrated, and sick. The men taunt him and treat him horribly.
2. Answers may vary. An example of a possible response:
   Imagery is used throughout paragraph 1. For example, the text states, "They growled and barked like detestable dogs, mewed, and flapped their arms and crowed." The sensory details describe sounds and visuals. Another example states, "...the ill treatment had flung him into a fever, which was fed by the inflammation of his parched and swollen throat and tongue." The imagery allows the reader to picture exactly what is happening in the scene.
3. B   4. D   5. D   6. A

WEEK 20

Monday

1. unique - positive
   strange - negative
2. spit - negative
   saliva - neutral
3. youthful - positive
   immature - negative
4. pushy - negative
   confident - positive
5. cheap - negative
   inexpensive - neutral
6. slender - positive
   scrawny - negative

Wednesday

Answers may vary. Examples of possible responses:
1. scent (positive); stench (negative)
2. chatty (positive); gossipy (negative)
3. bustling (positive); mobbed (negative)
4. petite (positive); stubby (negative)
5. statuesque (positive); giant (negative)
6. thrifty (positive); stingy (negative)

Friday

1. fair, attractive, pretty, beautiful, exquisite
2. overripe, bad, spoiled, rotten, putrid
3. unhappy, glum, sad, depressed, heartbroken
4. annoyed, aggravated, mad, furious, enraged
5. cool, crisp, cold, frigid, arctic
6. happy, joyful, delighted, ecstatic, euphoric

REFERENCE

https://poets.org/poem/day-0   Week 1, Friday

original Creative Commons article: Week 3, Wednesday
https://cnx.org/contents/7Mdj8HT3@1/What-Happened-to-the-Dolphins

https://poets.org/poem/stopping-woods-snowy-evening   Week 3, Friday

https://www.poetryfoundation.org/poems/52829/a-dream-within-a-dream   Week 7, Monday

http://www.gutenberg.org/ebooks/5230   Week 7, Friday

https://www.gutenberg.org/files/46/46-h/46-h.htm   Week 9, Monday

https://www.poemhunter.com/poem/jabberwocky   Week 9, Wednesday

original Creative Commons article: Week 9, Friday
https://cnx.org/contents/pMLyM9--@2/Chapultepec-Castle

original Creative Commons article: Week 11, Wednesday
https://cnx.org/contents/601ypon9@1/Ray-Brown

https://www.poetryfoundation.org/poems/44272/the-road-not-taken   Week 11, Friday

https://poets.org/poem/because-i-could-not-stop-death-479   Week 13, Monday

original Creative Commons article: Week 13, Wednesday
https://cnx.org/contents/h94JoJf-@1.3:DQ8WUzrX@4/The-Biography-of-Galileo-Galilei

original Creative Commons article: Week 15, Friday
https://cnx.org/contents/bNRXxzTK@10/Scott-Joplin

original Creative Commons article: Week 17, Wednesday
https://cnx.org/contents/-lXIwMsp@2/Flutes

https://www.poetryfoundation.org/poems/55687/the-song-of-wandering-aengus   Week 17, Friday

original Creative Commons article: Week 19, Wednesday
https://cnx.org/contents/l-DY5mRX@9/Classifying-Musical-Instruments#s22

argoprep.com

7th Grade

DIPLOMA

The certificate is presented to:

your name

by school name

for successful completion of ArgoPrep's Grade 7 ELA workbook

Signature

Date

Excellent work!

You have a purpose
You have a plan

God had it written
When your life began

You might be a Scientist, Lawyer or Doctor

Or maybe a Teacher, a Poet, an Author

You may lead a
City, a State or
the Nation

Perhaps you'll design the
world's greatest creation

There are songs to be written

Instruments to be played

Sports to tackle

Where points are made

A Mother, a Father, Counselor, Friend

The choices before you have a great end

Read His Word
And study His ways

God's hand is upon you
All of your days